THE
SOLAR
COOKBOOK
Recipes for a Sun-Cooked Diet

THE SOLAR COOKBOOK

Recipes for a Sun-Cooked Diet

By Stella Andrassy

EARTH BOOKS

A DIVISION OF MORGAN & MORGAN

EARTH BOOKS
a division of MORGAN & MORGAN, INC.
Publishers
145 Palisade Street
Dobbs Ferry, New York 10522

International Standard Book
Number 0-87100-142-X
Library of Congress Catalog
Card Number 79-88818

Printed in the United States of America

CONTENTS

ACKNOWLEDGMENTS

I want to thank all my friends who have encouraged me all these years and who have actually cooked with sunshine. They are in alphabetical order: Terry Arnold; Ursula Buchanan; Paula Chow; June Graffam; Ariadni Kapsalopoulou; Ann Merritt; Valerie Melusky; Alice Parker; Denyse Reid; Elizabeth Trolle; and Barbara Walker.

☆　　☆　　☆　　☆

There are no words with which I can thank my husband who has helped me thousands of times to take the sunstoves out of the garage, has focused them and patiently demonstrated them to innumerable visitors.

Stella Andrassy, 1981

AN INTRODUCTION TO COOKING WITH SUNSHINE

Since the dawn of time, man's fondest dream has been to harness the energy of the sun. During the centuries several attempts have been made to that effect, but it is only in recent years that this dream has become a reality.

Solar energy is being applied in a multitude of devices from the complicated solar cells that are used in the space vehicles to a humble solar stove, in which it is possible to boil, broil, bake and stew almost all foods that are cooked around the world.

To the Western cook—who is used to gas or electricity —the idea of cooking with sunshine may appear like science fiction.

And to the people, who live in the arid regions of Asia, Africa or South America, where there is a perpetual shortage of fuel, solar cooking may appear like sheer magic.

The fact is, however, that solar cooking is neither science fiction nor magic but a happy reality. Soon the people of the world will be able to cook most of their meals with *free fuel from the sky*.

Solar cooking can best be described as a combination of *mild broiling* and *oven baking*. In a way it also resembles the ancient art of cooking in *clay pots*. All recipes for clay pot cooking can be used in the sunstove, and also so can the clay pots—provided that the lids are blackened, or of a dark color.

Micro-Waves and Solar Cooking

For many years I was often puzzled over the phenomenon that foods continued to simmer and cakes to bake at temperatures *far below* those with which one could cook or bake in a conventional oven. This was a fact which I confirmed several times through comparative tests, using equal amounts of food, cooked in identical utensils.

In the summer of 1976, I finally got an explanation for this enigmatic behavior of my sunstove. My observations were not only confirmed but also scientifically explained by the noted Atlantic Research Corporation, who had acquired one of my sunstoves for analyzing purposes.

During the testing with scientific instruments, they found that when oil that was heated reached a temperature of 350 F, the oven temperature showed only 325 F. Such a temperature difference never occurs in a conventional oven (except maybe in a microwave oven). The presence of rays—like microwaves—in addition to the mild heat of the sun, may explain not only why suncooked food can cook at lower temperatures but also why suncooked food mostly tastes better than any food prepared with conventional methods.

Since in solar cooking in our sunstoves over-heating never occurs, the food cells do not burst, which makes meats juicier, it makes breads rise better, and cakes retain their moisture. No "hot spots" can develop and therefore there is no need to scour burnt pots and pans. All foods that can be cooked in a conventional oven can, with some adjustments, be cooked with the heat of the sun.

Solar Cooking and the Cook's Liberation

Because the fuel we use is sunshine—and nothing else —we can only master the art of solar cooking if we learn to watch the sky and adapt our cooking habits to the ever changing movements of the clouds. Thus, gradually we are compelled to prepare our daily bread in tune with the rhythm of nature—something many have become estranged from.

Solar cooking is a most relaxing occupation. Once the pots and pans are placed in the oven one can take it easy. Because the heat from the sun reaches the food mainly from *above* and not from *below—no food can get scorched, and no soup can boil over.* Further, little or no stirring is required.

There is yet another bonus from cooking with sunshine. If one goes shopping or visiting friends while the food is in the sunstove and only returns after a couple of hours, one will find that the cake is baked—but not dry. And the Boston Baked Beans have not burned to the bottom of the pan.

The explanation to this mystery is that the kind sun itself *turned off the heat* by moving along its path, and away from sending its rays directly into the oven. As soon as the window of the stove is not focused straight towards the sun, there is an automatic drop in temperature.

Advantages of Solar Cooking

There are many advantages in using solar energy for cooking:

1. No heat in, or from, the kitchen; thus the house will keep cooler and the air conditioning bills will be smaller.

2. Solar cooking saves on gas and electric bills, and conserves energy.

3. A solar oven provides leisurely outdoor cooking combined with agreeable outdoor living.

4. Solar cooked food tastes better than conventionally cooked food.

5. No over-cooking can take place, because the sun regulates its own heat input by moving on its own

path. No scorching of the food can take place; therefore much of the chore of scrubbing pots and pans is eliminated.

6. No fire hazards.

7. One can cook in the sunstove even if there is *snow lying on the ground,* provided there is clear bright sunshine.

A Suncooked Luncheon

My Sunday suncooked luncheons have become very popular. All the guests and family members are eager to get into the act. Some of my friends even bring along their own casseroles and pop them into the sunstove, while they wait for the result, basking in the bright sunshine by the pool. Thus, once a lady from Chile brought a big Jambalaya—a delectable dish made with shrimps, sliced ham, and tomatoes mixed with rice and spices. Some people add oysters and shredded cooked chicken. This very individual dish, that never is the same twice, this suncooked Jambalaya turned out to be an absolute success. For me the suncooked luncheons are a blessing, for they free me from slaving alone in a hot kitchen, while everybody is splashing around in a cool pool.

THE DEVELOPMENT OF
THE SUNSTOVE

How I Became Involved With Solar Cooking

My interest in solar energy and solar cooking goes far back in time. I began in 1952, when I had the privilege of meeting the Hungarian-born solar scientist, Dr. Maria Telkes, a pioneer in this, then, unusual field.

Dr. Telkes (who just had read a book I had written about her native country) asked me to assist her in writing a popular book on solar energy. My immediate reply was that I would be delighted to do so, but first I would have to learn something about the particular subject; the best place to do this would be at the Solar Research Laboratory of New York University of which she was the Director.

At first, I was only observing what was taking place in the laboratory, but in time, I began to assist in different chores. Now it so happened that Dr. Telkes received a grant from the Ford Foundation for the development of a solar cooking stove to be used in the arid tropical countries of the world.

Although Dr. Telkes was a brilliant chemist, her knowledge of the art of cooking was almost nil. She therefore asked me (who knew how to cook somewhat) if I would care to join her team and assist in the development of a sunstove and help to establish the technique of solar cooking. Without a moment's hesitation I jumped at this opportunity, for by then I had become completely fascinated with practical applications of solar energy and with all the benefits it could bring to mankind.

Since that day I have never stopped working with sunshine. Thus, during the years I have invented among other things:

A Solar Still, in which one can transform sea-water or polluted water into fresh drinking water.

A Solar Fruit and Vegetable Drier, in which the produce dries quickly and hygienically. It is now the market, and Morgan & Morgan, Inc. has published a book about how to build and operate this solar drier.

Lately, I have built a *solar cooking oven* which seems to be almost fool-proof. In this book you can read all about what this sunstove can produce, and how it must be operated so that it can absorb the maximum amount of solar energy. You can also read how to build a sunstove of your own.

The Story of the First Sunstoves

The *present* sunstove, which I am now using, was not built in a single day. Nor was the culinary art of cooking with sunshine mastered overnight.

During the last twenty-five years, I have assisted in building all kinds of different sunstoves, each experimental model representing some little improvement, only to be scrapped for a better idea. Through trials and errors—and lots of unbaked bread and grayish looking meats—we now finally have an almost ideal sunstove in which a great variety of dishes can be cooked to perfection.

The first solar cooking oven that I operated was designed by Dr. Maria Telkes in 1952. It was scientifically correct, and adequate temperatures for cooking were obtained, but the bread I baked in it did not get any color, and the chicken we tried to cook was best described as steamed. It was, however, *thoroughly* cooked.

This first sunstove had a *triangular* shape and was equipped with a black metal plate inserted under the double glass window. It was difficult to focus and often when I tilted it towards the sun, some of the food was spilled inside the oven.

However, at that time the triangular sunstove was all we had, thus, even if it was imperfect we continued with our experimental cooking. With painstaking perseverance all foods were carefully weighed and temperatures measured both in the oven, in the food, outside the oven, in full sunshine, as well as in the shadow.

The aim was to establish:

a) What basic foods can be cooked successfully in the sunstove?
b) The time required for their preparation?
c) What oven temperatures can be reached?
d) How can the device be improved?

Very quickly we were able to establish that we could cook rice, using standard measurements of 1 cup rice to 2 cups water.

Further we were able to cook a:

PORK and ONION STEW which became my stand-by for our early demonstrations.

   1 pound pork, cubed
   3 onions, minced finely
   1 tablespoon paprika
   1 clove garlic, crushed
   pepper and salt

The meat was tossed in the flour into which the spices had been mixed. It was placed, together with the onion and the garlic, in a rather high pot covered with a lid. Cooking time was 3 hours. In our present oven, patented in 1976, we can cook the same dish in about half this time.

An Improvement Is Made

During the first period of experimentation, our main objective was to prove that it is possible to cook with sunshine, and that it is not merely a scientific stunt. At that stage the aroma and appearance of the food was of secondary importance.

As time passed, I became bored with chicken that was steamed, instead of roasted, and with bread that looked unbaked, and even though they were completely cooked I nevertheless decided to find another way to upgrade our suncooked foods.

Often, during the experiments, I had noticed that if I pressed a thin slice of meat firmly against the inner metal sheet (underneath the glass window), I could get some brown color on the meat. The backside of this

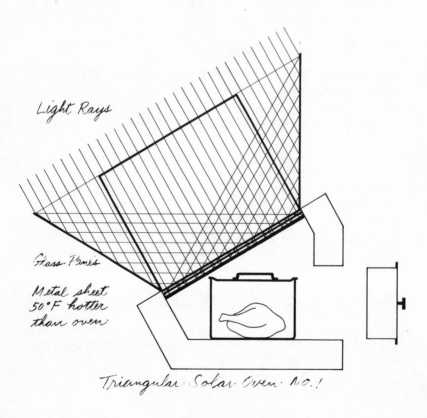

Light Rays

Glass Panes

Metal sheet 50°F hotter than oven

Triangular Solar Oven No. 1

metal sheet proved to be the hottest spot of the oven. When measured, we found it to be 50 °F hotter than the oven temperature. When this became evident, I removed the metal sheet and placed it as a lid above a pan in which I was baking bread. This method made all the difference. After one hour of baking, the bread had a golden crust. From that day on, I never had any trouble with color and appearance of any food.

Due to the triangular shape of the oven, we still had a problem with food spilling into the oven whenever it was tilted. Thus further improvements were needed.

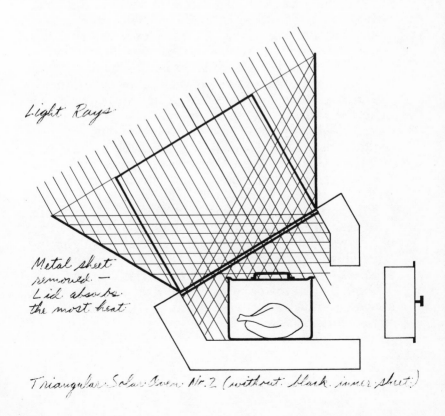

Light Rays

Metal sheet removed. — Lid absorbs the most heat

Triangular Solar Oven Nr. 2 (without black inner sheet.)

New Sunstoves are Developed

Meanwhile, at the Solar Laboratory of New York University, intense research and development continued. The main activities were centered around the construction of a more workable sunstove in which liquid food would not spill when the sunstove had to be re-oriented.

A variety of new designs were discussed and several new models were built, equipped with different means of keeping the food in a horizontal position during operation.

Among these new models was one designed in 1955-56 by an Iranian engineer, Fatalah Sotoodeh, a member of the solar team. This sunstove was equipped with a cooking pot which was suspended in such a way that it could swing freely, regardless of the oven shell movements.

Another innovation of this sunstove was that one could stir the food from above while it was cooking. Sotoodeh insisted that no Iranian woman would ever use a stove, if she could not get at the cooking pot from the top of the stove. He therefore designed an oven door behind the mirrors on top of the sunstove. This made the device needlessly heavy and cumbersome, but the cooking qualities of this stove were remarkably good.

During this period another sunstove was built. This one was made of cardboard and the mirrors were of metalized plastic. It was built in the summer of 1956.

This particular model was built on the insistence of a specialist in oriental cooking habits, who claimed that unless we could produce a sunstove that was light and "dirt cheap," there was not a chance to ever introduce solar cooking in the developing countries.

Later we had the opportunity to field-test both these, above described, sunstoves during a visit to the Navajo Indian Reservation.

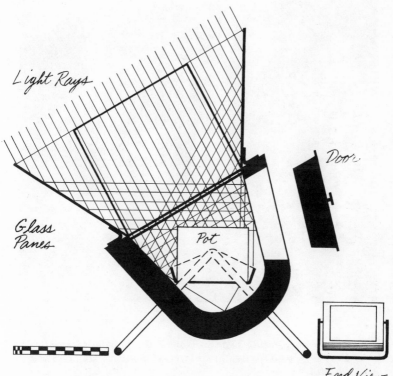

Light Rays

Glass
Panes

Pot

Door

End View

Sunstove with swinging inner platform

Here I am demonstrating solar cooking on the Navajo Reservation to Chief Grey-Eye, who showed great interest in my cooking and also in our solar still.

Solar Cooking on the Navajo Reservation

In 1956 Dr. Telkes received an invitation from the Bureau of Indian Affairs to visit the Navajo Reservation in Arizona. The aim of the visit was to make a study of the possibility of introducing solar cooking ovens and other solar devices among the 140,000 Navajos who lived on the reservation. One of their greatest problems was acquiring firewood for cooking and keeping warm during the bitter cold winters.

When Dr. Telkes asked me to accompany her in the summer of 1956 on this trip to demonstrate our solar cooking skills, I was absolutely delighted.

We first flew to Albuquerque, New Mexico; a small airplane then took us to Gallup, and from there the trip continued by truck far into the reservation.

Our destination was a place called *Many Farms*, which could be reached only by truck for the road was often not more than a trail in the sand.

It was a long, hot and dusty trip which took us through the desolate but beautiful landscape.

The morning after our arrival, a young Navajo woman, Carin Anderson, a Swedish sounding name, drove me to a trading post where we could buy all the ingredients needed for solar cooking Navajo foods.

My biggest surprise at the trading post came when the meat which we needed for a lamb stew was brought in. It certainly did not resemble any meat I had ever seen. It had a dark prune color and was hard like wood. In fact it was so bone-dry that it had to be cubed with a saw. Naturally this gave me grave doubts about how such meat could ever become tender. But as there was no other choice, I had to take it.

With bags full of vegetable and herbs, we returned to Many Farms where Dr. Telkes had focused the stoves so that they were warm enough to begin the solar cooking. It was mercilessly hot, over 100 degrees in the shade.

First came the lamb stew which Carin, who was an accomplished cook, prepared in no time—without using any measuring cups. I can therefore only describe how the stew was made and what went into it, not the quantities.

The lamb cubes were first dredged in flour and sauteed in lard together with sliced onions, a crushed clove of garlic, crushed dried juniper berries, and chili powder. While the meat was taking color, celery and squash were cut into cubes, and tomatoes were peeled. All this went into our black pot together with corn kernels.

While these preparations were taking place several young women arrived with their small children to visit the dispensary. In no time at all we were surrounded by a swarm of small interested on-lookers, staring at the sunstoves, as if they had been brought by an UFO.

Their amazement changed to joy when Carin made the dough for piñon cookies which I baked, non-stop, in the two other sunstoves. We couldn't work fast enough.

The sensation of the day came when Chief Grey-Eye himself arrived to inspect our efforts of putting the sun to work. Up to that time nobody among the non-Indian personnel of the Navajo Reservation had ever seen the Chief in person so they considered this visit a great honor.

Chief Grey-Eye nibbled thoughtfully on the piñon cookies we offered him, but when he asked to taste the lamb stew, I really got nervous for I was sure that the meat would be stone hard and inedible. But lo and behold! that bone-dry meat had become so soft that one could eat it with a spoon. *The mild rays of the sun can render even the toughest meats soft and juicy.*

It was not, however, the solar cooking which interested Chief Grey-Eye the most, but the solar distillation. This was most understandable for the scarce water on the reservation was often so contaminated that even the sheep died from drinking it.

The solar still, which aroused such a great interest, was constructed much like a glass covered picture frame.

Under the glass a black bath towel was suspended through which water could seep. For our demonstration we used the water from a local well which was kind of muddy and had a foul smell. To further dramatize the effect of solar distillation we poured a bottle of Coca-Cola into the pail with the well water. The Chief chuckled with pleasure when he sampled the crystal clear, distilled water which slowly seeped out from one of the spouts while the brown water-Coca-Cola mixture trickled out of the other spout.

Maria Telkes explaining how a solar still works. Coca-Cola was mixed with the feeding water in the pail to demonstrate the efficiency of the system.

On our last day on the reservation we baked Navajo bread with wild sage and tortillas which Carin kneaded, shaped, and slapped skillfully.

The sun-baking of the dry tortillas went off very well. It was only when a visiting anthropologist from Mexico insisted that I fry tostadas, a kind of tortilla, in deep fat that everything went wrong.

To be honest, it was not the fault of the anthropologist nor of the tostadas but of the sunstove which I used. This was the "light and dirt cheap" variation, made of cardboard and plastic mirrors which we had been urged to design in New York. It was sure light enough, for just when the fat began to sizzle, a sudden strong wind-gust lifted the stove from the table, turning it up side down and spilling all the hot oil over my bare legs. Whereafter the stove sailed off on its mirror wings and landed in a dry pond.

Since that day I have never built a light-weight sunstove again. A sunstove in which one can bake, boil, stew and cook is a fine instrument which must stand up to exposure in all types of weather and wind. Therefore, it must be heavy and sturdy, but it must also be mobile so that it can be handled easily and can be brought in shelter at night and during spells of bad weather. (Recipes tested on the Navajo trip include Navajo Chili Pork—see Meat recipes, Navajo Bread with Wild Sage—see Bread and Cakes, and Piñoñ Cookies, see Desserts.)

A NEW SUNSTOVE GETS
FIELD TESTED

As time passed, a new type of sunstove was constructed which was in many ways superior to all previous models. This sunstove had a cylindrical body, with a swinging inner platform so no food could spill into the oven. It was sturdy and relatively easy to operate and had excellent cooking properties. It was developed at N.Y.U. in 1955-56.

In fact, this new model was so satisfactory that the United Nations Food and Agricultural Organization decided to acquire several sunstoves of this type for field-testing around the world. Thus, sunstoves of this design were sent to Thailand, Egypt, and Italy. I personally brought the stove intended for the Caribbean Commission to Trinidad in the autumn of 1957, at the invitation of the Governor General, Mr. J. Heesterman, who during a visit to New York had seen one of these sunstoves in operation.

Over 20 years ago Mr. Heesterman, a farseeing man, understood the importance of solar energy for the Caribbean Islands where there was either little or no fuel available, and was eager in helping to introduce it.

It was during my stay on Trinidad that I made a unique discovery with the sunstove: I found out that under certain circumstance it is possible to cook "without sunshine."

Solar Cooking Without Sunshine

When I told my friends—who knew something about solar energy—that I had cooked without sunshine, they all exclaimed: "That is impossible!" for according to all rules, no one should try to cook with a sunstove, if the sky is so overcast that no shadows are visible.

Nevertheless, in spite of that golden rule, I succeeded in *cooking without sunshine*—even if it was not my intention to do so. This incident took place in Trinidad, in the fall of 1957, after I had arrived there with the new sunstove.

My first demonstration took place under very official circumstances. The stove was placed in the middle of the lawn, right in front of the main building of The Caribbean Commission. It was a beautiful spot surrounded with large flaming red poinsettias. The sun was shining and there was not a breath of wind.

The stove—with its mirrors reflecting the blue sky— was surrounded by officials of all kinds, social workers and home economists. One of the home economists prepared a native dish for the demonstration, consisting of: cubed veal, rolled in a paste of crushed garlic and spices which we roasted in butter together with sliced onions. This roasting/simmering took about one hour.

Everything was going fine and the cook expert had just added: cubed sweet potatoes, okra and tomato sauce to the large black pot, when suddenly dark clouds began to overshadow the sun. I glanced at the sky and saw thick clouds rolling in, at high speed, from the sea. At this moment somebody from the office came out and said that they had just received a first hurricane warning over the radio.

This was indeed bad news for me for I knew that we would need at least one hour more to get this dish ready. And now, because of those clouds, I was compelled to interrupt the demonstration.

"What a fiasco!" I thought to myself. "I came this long way with all expenses involved, and then my first attempt to show that one can cook with sunshine goes sour."

Heartbroken, I left the sunstove standing on the lawn and went into the office for a conference with Mr.

Heesterman. Mr. Heesterman had seen the sunstove work in New York and was not troubled over the unfavorable weather report. His great concern was whether we could produce fresh water from sea water with solar energy. There was a great need for fresh water on several islands under his jurisdiction, particularly on the Caicos Islands.

While we were discussing desalinization of sea water, which I was keenly interested in, the time seemed to fly. We must have been talking for over an hour when suddenly a young man from the office burst in with an agitated voice: "The sunstove!—The sunstove!" I became quite perplexed, for I knew that the sunstove could neither burn nor explode and under this miserable cloudy sky, no cooking could go wrong.

"The food is ready!—It is perfect!" the young man exclaimed.

As we received this incredible information, we all went promptly into the garden, which was in full shadow, to sample the food that had *cooked without sunshine*.

It was exactly as the man said: The food was ready and it was perfect! The veal was soft as butter and the vegetable cooked, yet *firm*, which is a peculiarity of solar cooking.

I must admit that this turn of circumstances was a great relief to me. After all—my first solar cooking demonstration had not been such a poor show, as I had feared.

Now the explanation of the phenomenon that one can cook under a completely overcast sky, is that in tropical regions certain rays of the solar spectrum have sufficient power to penetrate through the clouds enabling cooking to continue, even without direct sunshine.

Although it was very important to know that in equatorial regions it is possible to "cook without sunshine," I would not recommend cooking or baking unless a clear shadow is visible and the little squares on the corners of the frame of the sunstove are perfectly sunlit. (See page 52.)

A few days later, I left Trinidad for Brazil and other South American countries. The sunstove remained for the field-tests and a home economist was to conduct cooking experiments with native foods of the Caribbean area, under different weather conditions and at all times of the year. For over two years we received regular weather reports and results of the cooking which was extremely helpful for our research. Among other things we discovered two defects to our stove which cooked so well in Trinidad. It turned out to be difficult to orient, and its legs were too weak for its weight. Further improvement was now needed.

A KIND OF SUN SAGA

The Curtiss-Wright Episode 1958-1960

Solar energy has always been the Cinderella among the sciences. Almost until this very day, this research has been relegated to small and widely dispersed laboratories, operating with pitifully small funds. Experienced solar scientists are therefore scarce and by nature mostly self-taught.

One such scientist was the brilliant solar pioneer, Dr. Maria Telkes. The solar laboratory at New York University, where we did our research, was certainly nothing to write home about. It was housed in a small building made of sheet metal which, according to the season, was cold in winter but unbearably hot in summer.

Thus, for us who were working in that laboratory, it seemed like a fairy tale when Roy Hurley, Chairman of the Board of the Curtiss-Wright Corporation (best known for its airplane and motor fabrication), came in person to inspect our research activities.

When Mr. Hurley tasted my suncooked Shrimp Curry, saw the solar stills functioning, and the solar driers filled with dehydrating fruits and vegetables, he became so fascinated with the enormous potential of solar energy, that he decided right then and there that Curtiss-Wright would be the first large industrial body in the world to enter into the solar field. This took place in the spring of 1958.

Once the decision was made, it took no time for Curtiss-Wright to take over the entire solar laboratory from New York University, complete with scientists, technicians, instruments, and models.

Roy Hurley's plan was to create the most elaborate solar research center the world had ever seen at the C.W. Division, Princeton, New Jersey.

The "Sun Court", as the establishment was called, was erected around an open plaza where a large solar heated swimming pool was installed, a solar operated fountain was playing and a solar operated radio beamed music. In short, it was a solar scientist's dream come true.

The main building was 100% solar heated and kept its temperature through a chemical heat storage, which was one of Dr. Telkes' inventions. The solar collectors for the hot water in the building and for the swimming pool were made after my designs.

Among my many duties was to supervise and plan the solar cooking and solar dehydration of fruits and vegetables.

The *outdoor solar kitchen* deserves to be described: It was designed by the late Professor Aladar Olgyay, who was not only an exceptionally fine architect but also a solar scientist, a rare combination.

To the main building he had added a partly covered patio, which functioned as an extended kitchen. Here the cook could sit in the shadow, while the sunstove was exposed to full sunshine. The patio roof gave protection to the sunstove during nights and periods of bad weather.

On the Sun Court, batteries of sunstoves and solar driers were kept in constant operation. Helpers chopped and sliced vegetables and fruits. We cooked mainly American foods, upon which Mr. Hurley placed particular emphasis, in view of a U.S. market for sunstoves. Every ingredient was weighed and analyzed, and we had no problem finding voluntary test panels. In addition to these activities, solar stills and solar pumps were built, tested, and operated. Scores of experts and technicians collected all data. No effort or expense was spared.

Needless to say, the sunstove was further improved at Curtiss-Wright. The result was a handsome oven with good cooking properties. Not surprisingly the first

Curtis-Wright stove also left room for improvement. In particular it collapsed in heavy winds, and its mirrors would fall out.

During the time that we were working on the completion of this fantastic establishment it was kept a company top secret. No journalist was permitted on the premises, and all who were assigned to the project were sworn to secrecy.

But, alas, just when everything was ready and we had practiced for the grand inauguration of the Sun Court, everything collapsed. In early 1960 the far-sighted Roy Hurley was voted out by the stockholders; in other words, he was fired. The result of this was that just as quickly as Curtiss-Wright Corporation had entered the solar field, it got out of it again. Not only was the entire solar program terminated, but the new management of Curtiss-Wright sold the Princeton Divison to Shell Oil Company who needed more ground for expansion.

Thus, the beautiful and efficient solar complex was razed to the ground. The scientists, with their unique knowledge, were dismissed and dispersed in all directions. The solar heated swimming pool was filled in and the site converted into a parking lot. The valuable instruments and solar devices, among them all the sunstoves, were sent to the garbage dump.

And so finished one of the finest endeavors ever made by any large industrial corporation to harness the energy of the sun.

My Home is My Laboratory

Although the demolishment of the solar research project at Curtiss-Wright came as a blow to all involved, it did not dampen my fervent belief in the practical use of solar energy. I was determined to continue my work—even if I had to do it all alone.

Luckily, this was not to be the case, for my husband, an engineer and agricultural expert, decided to help me

A happy day for solar cooking! Here I have just removed the legs from the sunstove and placed the oven-body in a cradle, made of wood. This simple device made it possible to focus the stove more accurately towards the sun. From now on solar cooking was easy.

in my work and to install a solar laboratory on our small farm situated about six miles from Princeton University. Solar-Electric Laboratories was established in spring, 1960.

Here we have been working as a team, having almost no outside help whatsoever. The sunny garden became an ideal Outdoor Solar Laboratory, and the basement of our little house was converted to an Indoor Solar Laboratory. Thus, my home became my laboratory.

One of our first efforts was to make the Curtiss-Wright model more workable. The first improvements consisted of removing the legs from the stove and placing the oven-body in a cradle-like stand, which prevented the stove from tipping over.

Further, this cradle enabled one to focus the stove towards the Sun more accurately than hitherto ever had been possible.

From then on solar cooking became much easier, and I dared to cook without watching the clock or thermometers.

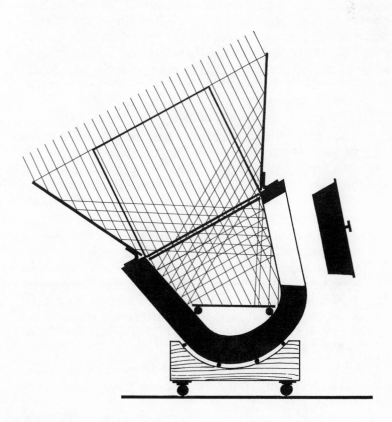

A Simple Sunstove

I have always firmly believed in the saying: "It is better to teach a man how to fish than to give him a fish."

With this in mind I set out, in 1961, to build a sunstove which was so simple and uncomplicated that it could be built by anyone from readily available materials and at little cost. This stove, made of a wicker basket lined with adobe, was heavy and cumbersome but it worked! And it really was "dirt cheap" which was a necessity if a sunstove was ever to be used in the developing countries. I shall describe this wicker-adobe stove in some detail. A detailed description of a different sunstove, which can easily be built at home, will be given in the section called "Building Your Own Sunstove." The adobe and wicker India stove is recommended as a do-it-yourself stove for areas where aluminum sheet, mylar, and fiberglass insulation are too expensive or not available. The *sunnet* do-it-yourself model is especially suitable for the U.S.A.

The stove was made as follows:

1. The body of this sunstove was made of a square wicker laundry hamper. The inside of the basket was lined with a layer of adobe (or clay) about 1¼ inch thick. To make the clay absorb the heat from the sun better, I covered its wet surface with charcoal powder which made it black.

2. As it was impossible for me to cut an oven door in the basket, I solved this problem though using the "sun window" as the door. The frame for the window was made of wood and was wired to the basket. A second inner frame was hinged and covered with a double layer of heat resistant plastic film. (Glass would have been better, but is heavier and more breakable.)

3. The mirrors were made of reflective aluminum. (Mirrors or highly polished copper could have been used.)

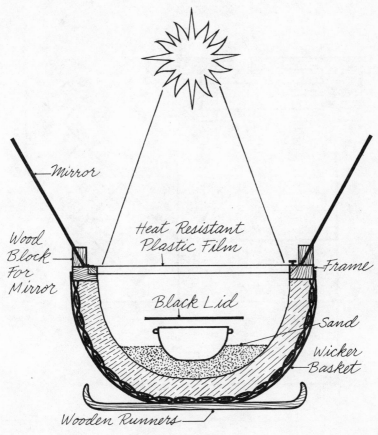

Mirror

Wood
Block
For
Mirror

Heat Resistant
Plastic Film

Frame

Black Lid

Sand

Wicker
Basket

Wooden Runners

Note: Instead of adobe, cement can be used.

Detail of frame for glass

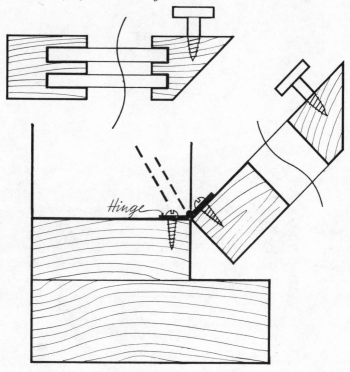

Hinge

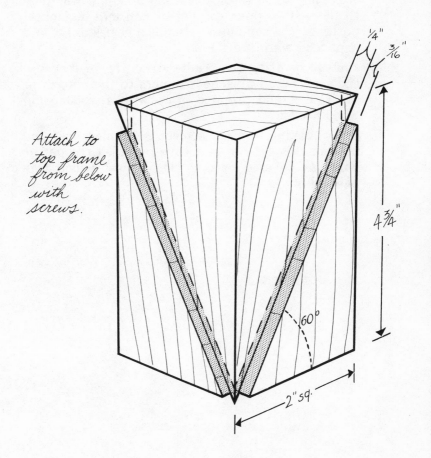

Attach to top frame from below with screws.

¼"

3/16"

4¾"

60°

2" sq.

4. In this basket-adobe sunstove I did not use a platform for holding pots and pans, but I poured in a layer of sand darkened with charcoal. Whenever the stove had to be tilted towards the sun, it was relatively easy to push the pot or pan in a horizontal position. The sand also acted as a heat-storage and kept food warm for a long time.

5. Instead of using the cradle structure for focusing the sunstove, I attached runners to the bottom of the basket and propped it up with a wooden log when needed.

6. Most cooking utensils (except high ones) could be used in this type of sunstove provided the pot or pan was covered with a metal sheet which was painted black.

The New Solar Generation

One day while I was conducting a solar cooking seminar at the "Y" in Princeton, a group of third graders from Miss Mason's School came to witness the demonstration and to sample the results from the sunstove.

The enthusiasm of the children was very refreshing. Nothing could express it better than some of the letters that I received afterward.

These kids needed no more proof. After they had tasted the sunbaked chicken and chocolate cake* they knew that the sun worked.

In order to educate the new solar generation, I hope that gradually all schools will own a sunstove and a solar drier for fruits and vegetables. Nothing could be more instructive for a child than to see the sun at work. When the children get older they will be able to understand much better the principles of solar energy.

Miss Mason's School
September 26, 1977

Dear Countess Andrassy,

Thank you for showing us the solar oven. Thank you for telling us how it worked. It was interesting. The chicken was very good. The oven was hotter than I thought. The cake was very good too. I am glad you could make it. I hope you make more and sell them. The solar oven looked neat. It looked hard to make. I hope you make more. I had a fun time there.

Sincerely,
Kipper Largo

Miss Mason's School
September 30, 1977

Dear Countess Andrassy,

Thank you for making my day by letting us [see] your solar oven. That was such a delicious cake and chicken. It was as good as my mother's cake. It is amazing how much heat gets in the oven.
I wish I could do something like that.

Sincerely,
Josie Robins

Miss Mason's School
September 30, 1977

Dear Countess Andrassy,

Thank you for the chicken. It was good. The solar oven was neat. The cake was good. I wish I had one. It was hot.

Sincerely,
Seth Woodward

*Note: The recipe for the chicken I cooked will be found under Sunbaked Chicken, p. 70. I always used Ann Page Chocolate Mix, which bakes in about 45 minutes to 1 hour.

BUILDING YOUR OWN SUNSTOVE

The SUNNET Sunstove
Designed for Do-it-Yourselfers

Sunstoves are—as yet—not items you can readily buy at your friendly hardware store. So, if you want to cook with sunshine—and if you are a handy person—you can find here a description of how to build a sunstove yourself. But bear in mind, that even to build a plain stove, like the Sunnet, requires accuracy and precision. Each part of the oven has been carefully designed at this laboratory (Solar Electric Laboratories, Kingston, New Jersey) according to the basic principles of sunstove construction.*

The main components of this sunstove are:

a) An *inner oven*, made of aluminum sheet.

b) An *outer oven shell* made of ¼ inch plywood.

c) A *glass window* with reflectors.

A list of all materials and tools is to be found on the next page. When finished, the stove can be placed on any table or even on the ground for use. It weighs about ten pounds. Before starting on the project, be sure to have all materials and tools at hand. Then make a paper pattern in full scale of all the parts, before tracing it on the aluminum or wood material. As an old hand at sunstove building I always make a mock-up model of card-board to be certain that all parts fit together, before I cut, or saw, into expensive materials.

*Full scale plans of the *Sunnet* sunstove can be obtained by writing to Morgan & Morgan, Inc., 145 Palisade Street, Dobbs Ferry, New York 10522.

Materials

Inner Oven Shell: Aluminum Sheet. Thickness: 0.22*

Outer Oven Shell: Plywood. Thickness: ¼-inch (preferably).

Glass: 2 panels, 14½×14½-inch. Thickness: single strength. American window glass.

Reflectors: Silvered MYLAR plastic, cemented to 4 panels, 14×14 inches, of ³/₁₆-inch plywood. If Mylar is not available a shiny metal such as aluminum will also work.

Top Frame: Kiln-dried wood, 2×1 inch, in two 18 inch lengths, and two 14 inch lengths.

Door and Door Frame: Kiln-dried wood, 2×1-inch.

Spacers, Studs, Supports: Kiln-dried wood.

Insulation: Fiberglass (preferably Ultrafine, without binder.)

8 Elbow Irons.

4 Right angle-irons.

3 Handles.

Screws, wing-nuts, cement, caulking paint.

Hand Tools Used For Construction of Stove

1. Hammer
2. Hand saw
3. Hand bender
4. Sheet metal snipe
5. Vise
6. Pliers
7. Drill
8. Screw driver

It is assumed that jig and other labor saving accessories are available as well as patterns.

Have all materials available and cut, drilled and bent before commencing the work.

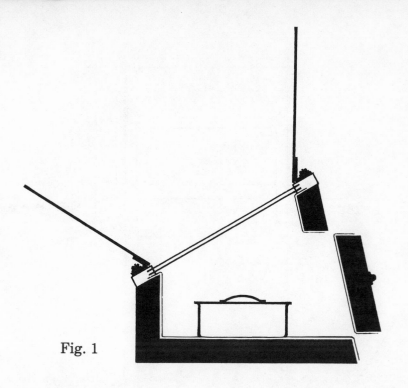

Fig. 1

The diagram of the stove is shown in Figure 1. The window of this unit is tilted at a 30° angle with the horizon, which is a favorable tilt for latitudes south of the thirty-eighth parallell in the U.S. Further south or higher north, other tilts (S. 12°—N. 45°) may be better.

Inner Oven Shell

The inner oven shell can be cut out in one piece from a sheet of *aluminum* (Figure 2). Allow ¾ inch for flanges.

Trace the pattern on the aluminum sheet and carefully mark the bends.

Drill the holes in the flanges before bending or notching.

Screw the sides together with sheet metal screws, size 6, 32, ¼ inch long, selftapping aluminum.

Bend the top flange at a 30 degree angle and attach below it a 2×1" wooden lath, 14 inches long.

Attach similar 14 inches long 2×1 wooden laths below each of the other appropriately bent flanges.

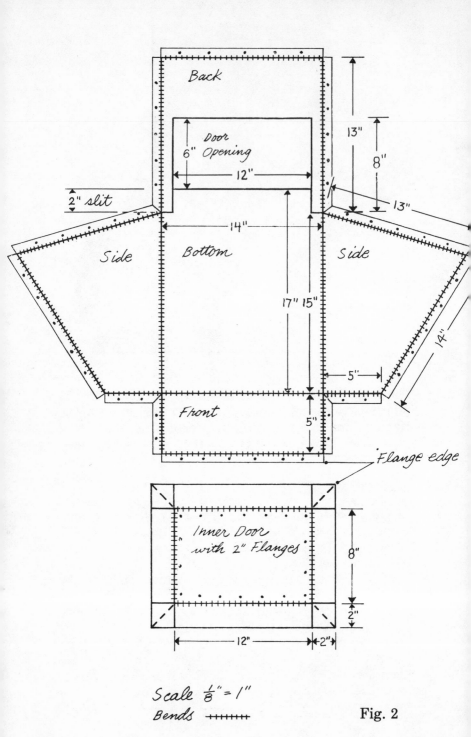

Back

Door Opening

6"

12"

13"

8"

13"

2" slit

14"

Side

Bottom

Side

17" 15"

14"

5"

Front

5"

Flange edge

Inner Door
with 2" Flanges

8"

2"

12"

2"

Scale $\frac{1}{8}" = 1"$
Bends ++++++

Fig. 2

44

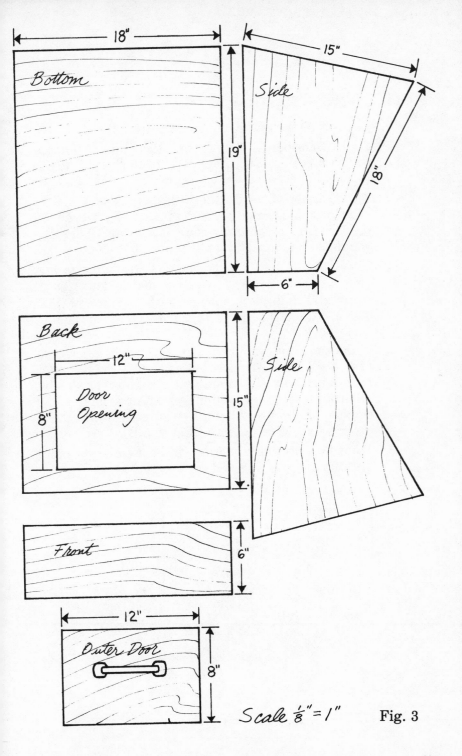

Scale ⅛" = 1"   Fig. 3

45

Outer Oven Shell: Made of ¼ inch Plywood

1. Cut out all parts, as shown on Figure 3.
2. Screw together the front, the sides and the bottom to the 4 corner studs, appropriately slanted at the tops.
3. To the inside of the *bottom*, add 2 cross bars—19 inches long, 2 inches high and 1 inch wide, in order to prevent the insulation from collapsing under the weight of the inside oven (Figure 4).
4. Cement and screw together the tapered *door frame*, consisting of 2 wood bars 14 inches long 2×1" wood, and 2 bars 8 inches long of 2×1" wood (Figure 5). Attach this frame to the inner side of the plywood back.
5. Make the *door* of similar tapered design consisting of 2 wood bars 12 inches long 2×1" wood, and 2 bars 6 inches 2×1" wood, but 1 millimeter smaller all around. Screw on aluminum sheet to inside and cement the sides: fill with insulation and attach plywood sheet to outside (Figure 5 B).
6. Paint all woodwork inside with heat-resistant paint and the outside with out-door paint.

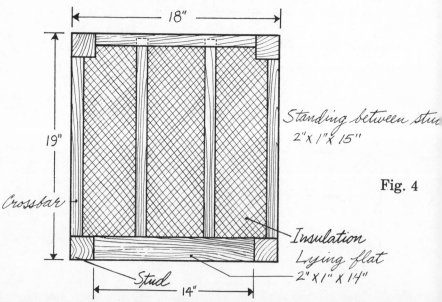

18"

19"

14"

Standing between stu

2" x 1" x 15"

Fig. 4

Crossbar

Insulation
Lying flat
2" x 1" x 14"

Stud

2" x 1" x 14"

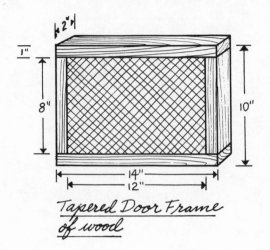

Tapered Door Frame of wood

Fig. 5

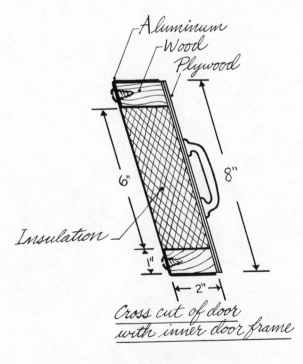

Cross cut of door with inner door frame

Fig. 5B

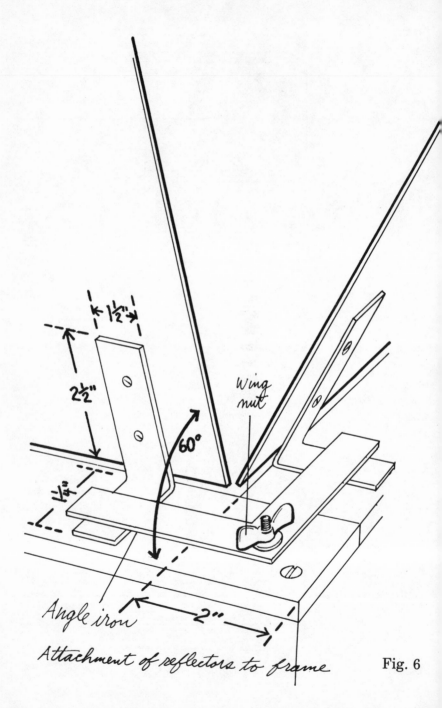

1½"

2½"

¼"

60°

Wing
nut

Angle iron

2"

Attachment of reflectors to frame

Fig. 6

Reflectors

One of the thorniest problems when building any type of sunstove is the mounting of the reflectors, because the efficiency of the stove depends greatly upon the mirrors staying in a fixed position at a 60° angle. It is also desirable to remove the mirrors when the stove is not in use.

The reflectors of this model consist of four mirrors, each 14×14". They are made of silvered Mylar cemented to a $^3/_{16}$ inch thick plywood sheet, also 14×14". Further 8 elbow irons are needed: 2½×1¼×1½ inch bent to an angle of 60 degrees. Drill 2 holes in the 2½ inch bend. Paint the back of the plywood and attach 2 elbow irons to each sheet. Finally, cement the silvered Mylar to the front and put a tape round the edges (optional).

These 4 mirrors are then attached to the top frame through the angle iron, and held in place with a wing nut screw (Figure 6).

Top Frame

The wooden frame has an outer dimension of 18 inches and an inner dimension of 14 inches. It is built of four pieces of 2×1 inch wood. The inside of each part has two ¼ inch deep grooves for the glass panes (Figure 7). The glass panes should fit rather loosely in the grooves to avoid cracking during heating.

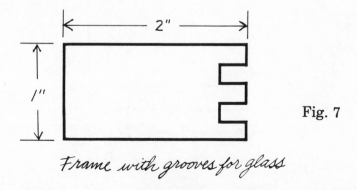

Fig. 7

Frame with grooves for glass

In order to facilitate the installment of the glass—or replace it if broken, or if it needs cleaning—the top piece of the frame is removable (Figure 8 and Figure 9).

Drill holes for corner 2 inch long screws and the wing-nut screws. Paint the frame and join the three pieces together.

Assembling

When all the separate parts are ready, as described, place the top frame *face down* on a table and put the inner oven upside down atop. Now screw the flanges of the inner oven to the wooden frame, on three sides. —Turn—

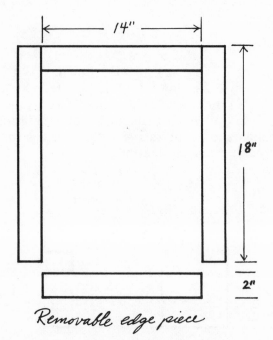

Removable edge piece

Fig. 8

Slide the inner oven into the outer shell (being careful not to shift the insulation). Attach the back of the oven to which the door frame was screwed and all empty spaces filled with insulation to the main body of the oven. Fasten corner screws.

Starting from the top, slide the glass panes into the grooves and close the frame with the removable piece which gets held with 2 screws from the top of the frame and a tape. Fasten the angle irons on each corner and mount the mirrors, fastening them with the iron angles. Close the plug door. Caulk all cracks before painting.

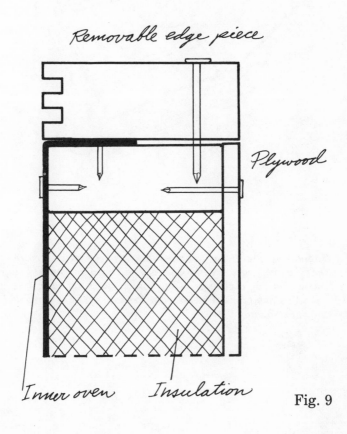

Fig. 9

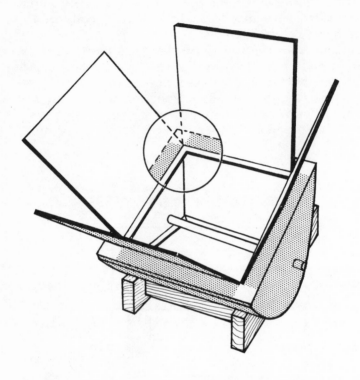

There is no doubt that the sunstove has been focused correctly when
the shadows cast by the mirrors fall straight on the top of the
frame—leaving a clearly visible sunlit square on each of its corners.
All adjustments must be relevant to these sunlit squares which function as small sun-dials.

USING THE SUNSTOVE

The sunstove, which I am now using, is basically a "hot-box" equipped with mirrors which reflect the rays of the sun through a glass window into the interior of the oven—where the concentrated rays develop sufficient heat for baking or cooking almost any food. It is easy to reach oven temperatures of 300-350 °F in this vicinity, just south of New York City. But in Arizona and other southern states I have often seen oven temperatures reach 475 °F.

Turning Position of the Sunstove

Orientation and Tilting

The sunstove differs from conventional cooking stoves insofar as it must be moved (about once every hour) in order to permit the maximum amount of solar energy to be collected in the interior of the oven. This is obtained only when the sunrays can fall unhampered straight through the glass window.

How to be Sure that the Sunstove is Receiving Optimum Sunshine

There is no doubt that the sunstove has been focused correctly when the shadows from the mirrors fall straight on the top of the frame—leaving a clearly visible *sunlit square* on each of its corners. All adjustments must be relevant to these sunlit squares which function as small sun-dials.

Solar Cooking Utensils
2 black pans and 2 black lids
have many applications

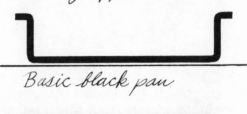

Basic black pan

Upside down for baking

Pan frying - small lid

Stew - large lid

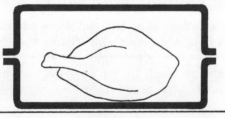

10 Golden Rules for Successful Solar Cooking

1. Before starting to cook with the sunstove—observe the sky! If it is a *very* hazy day, or *heavy* clouds are appearing on the horizon, then it is not advisable to try to cook with sunshine that day.

2. Pre-heat the oven, and read the oven thermometer. Don't start cooking until the thermometer reads 300 °F or more. This takes approximately one hour, depending upon ambient temperature and time of year.

3. All cooking utensils should be *black*, for black absorbs the heat of the sun better than any other color. All pots and pans must have tight fitting lids. They should be *shallow*, so the mild heat of the sun can better penetrate the food. For the same reason, the food should not be heaped thickly, but spread in a thin layer. It is better to use *two* shallow pans, rather than one high pot filled to the brim with food.

4. Meats and vegetables cook faster if thinly sliced or cut into small cubes.

5. Use little or no water when cooking meats or vegetables: they contain sufficient moisture, and very little liquid evaporates during solar cooking.

6. Don't stir the food needlessly (in solar cooking, food can not get scorched). Each time the oven door is opened some of the heat escapes.

7. Soak legumes (beans, peas, lentils, etc.) overnight, in order to speed up the cooking time. Rice, millet, barley, etc. also cook faster if they are pre-soaked.

8. Take your time. When one cooks with sunshine one must acquire another attitude towards time. The sun decides the timing—not the chef. On a sunny day it will take exactly the same time to bake a

cake, or cook rice, as in a conventional oven, but early in the morning—in the late afternoon—or on a cold day, more time is required. *Patience* is the key word. Nothing worse can happen than that one must finish the dish in the indoor kitchen.

9. Don't forget to use pot-holders! The oven is much hotter than one thinks it could possibly be. I have seen the thermometer showing 475 °F; and a friend has experienced 500 °F in her oven in New Mexico. If the temperature is too high for any special dish— just turn the stove slightly out of focus.

10. In case the food is ready before you are ready to serve it, simply remove the mirrors and cover the glass window with a pillow or blanket. This method turns the sunstove into a veritable "hot-box" in which food can be kept piping hot for hours.

Care and Upkeep of the Sunstove

Although the sunstove is a sturdy device, it is a fine instrument which deserves to be well cared for.

1. Never leave the sunstove out in rain or at night. If possible keep it under a roof, in a shed or garage, when not in use, protected with a plastic or other cover.

2. When not in use, remove the mirrors. Keep them stacked with a soft cloth or paper between to avoid scratching the surface.

3. Never polish the mirrors, but wipe them with a soft cloth. If necessary wash them with a mild soap. They keep for years, and don't lose their shine if well taken care of.

DON'TS

Now, after having told about so many dishes that *can* be cooked in the sunstove the time has come to talk about what *not* to cook.

Don't try deep frying in oil or fat. Deep frying requires very high heat from the bottom of the pan or cooking pot, and that is not available in the sunstove, where the mild heat reaches the top of the food first.

For the same reason, don't cook food which demands rapidly boiling water. This is explained in the recipe for cooking macaroni.

Never try to cook food which requires constant stirring. Examples of foods to avoid are: sauces like Bearnaise or Hollandaise; they can curdle even on the most modern, conventional stove.

I don't recommend thin pancakes like "crepes" or French omelets, which demand very exact heat and quick movements.

I never tried a soufflé for I was sure that if a cloud should cover the sun, it would turn into a pancake.

Many Chinese and Japanese dishes, which call for very high bottom heat and constant stirring do not lend themselves to solar cooking.

These are examples. Principally, no food which requires exceedingly high temperatures and much stirring should be cooked in the sunstove.

Some Cooking Times and Temperatures*

Item	Time (hours)	Temperature
Beans	4	300°
Beef Stew (1 pound)	2¾	275°
Lentil Soup	1½	300°
Frozen Codfish	3	275°
Chicken (3 pounds)	2	300°
Chicken Breasts	1½	310°
Franks (cooked in black foil)	½	290°
Hamburgers (cooked in special cooker with preheated lid)	¼	290°
Pork Loin (3½ pounds)	3	300°
Squash	2	500°
Soy Bread	1	500°
Scrambled Eggs	½	300°
Peach Jam	4	300°

*Excerpted from the experimental data sheets provided in the appendix. Note that the times and temperature given are examples of actual suncooking. Because so much depends on the weather conditions, ambient temperature, time of year, and so on, no precise times for solar recipes can be given.

Ready Mix Baking Tests

The following list gives an idea of the time, temperatures and weather conditions we had when baking with some standard "Ready-Mixes."

Date	Type of Product	Time	Oven Temp. F°		Weather
			In	Out	
Aug. 20	Rolls: Brown & Serve	0:40	350	350	Clear
Sept. 15	Rolls: Brown & Serve	1:00	275	300	Slight Haze
Oct. 2	Butterscotch Cookies (Pillsbury Ice Box)	0:45	275	275	Clear
Oct. 7	Butterscotch Cookies (Pillsbury Ice Box)	0:25	350	350	Clear
Oct. 9	Spice Cake (Pillsbury)	1:05	300	300	Hazy
Oct. 9	Biscuits (Bisquick)	1:00	280	295	Hazy
Oct. 10	Biscuits (Bisquick)	0:55	300	300	Clear
Oct. 16	Coconut Cookies (Pillsbury)	1:20	275	300	Slight Haze
Oct. 17	Pineapple Cake Mix (Pillsbury)	1:15	275	265	Clear
Oct. 7	Orange Cake Mix (Pillsbury)	0:47	300	275	Clear

Please note that the oven temperature often showed around 275°F.

Summary

In this book it has been described how the sunstove developed from the first, unwieldy stove to the present model, which is practically fool-proof.

Descriptions and instructions are also given on how a simple inexpensive sunstove can be built. The main difference between solar and conventional cooking is that one must use less liquid and cut meats and vegetables finer than usual. The recipes collected in this book have all been thoroughly tested. They derive from all corners of the world; some I have collected myself during my many travels abroad and some have been given to me by my foreign friends, for which I am very grateful.

Any food which can be boiled, baked, braised or stewed in any ordinary oven can, with some slight changes, be successfully cooked in the sunstove.

Fuel is becoming expensive and scarce—at least in many countries. It is therefore time to begin to save on our dwindling resources, and to replace them with solar energy wherever this is possible. Solar cooking is an enjoyable way to begin.

RECIPES

SOUPS

Soups come in all sorts of varieties: many require hours of cooking—particularly Bean Soups. This naturally uses a lot of expensive gas or electricity. An obvious solution is to cook soups in the sunstove, where the fuel is free and it does not matter if the soup keeps simmering for half a day or more.

Soups can be economical and when served with a wholesome bread and cheese—and fruit as dessert—a soup becomes a well balanced and satisfying meal.

Another attractive characteristic of soup is that it does not matter if it is kept waiting; many soups are even tastier when reheated or served the next day.

BRAZILIAN BLACK BEAN SOUP

A dish that is ideal for the sunstove because of the long slow-cooking time requirement.

1½ cups dried black beans	½ cup red wine
¾ pound chorizos (a garlic seasoned sausage)	1 onion, minced
2 slices bacon, cubed	1 clove garlic, finely minced or crushed
1¾ pounds lean pork or beef, cut in 2 inch cubes	2 tablespoons oil
½ cup orange juice	Chili pepper and salt to taste

Soak the beans overnight. Drain and cover with fresh water. Add the onion and garlic and cook in a covered pot for at least 2 hours. Place the meat, sausage (left whole) and bacon in a small amount of water, bring to a boil, and simmer for about 5 minutes. Add the meats to the beans and simmer for another 2 hours. Add the orange juice and wine and simmer for an additional 30 minutes. Remove the sausage and slice in ½ inch rounds. Save some rounds for decoration and return the remainder to the pot. Correct seasoning and stir. Serve on a bed of rice and decorate the beans with slices of oranges and sausage.

WHITE BEAN SOUP

1 cup dried white beans, soaked overnight	1 small carrot, whole
5 cups water	1 bay leaf
1 teaspoon salt	pinch of thyme
1 large onion studded with one clove	1 celery rib, whole
	1 cup scalded milk
	2 tablespoons butter

Combine beans, water, salt and vegetables in a pot and simmer for about 3 hours under cover, or until beans are very tender. Remove from sunstove. Discard carrot, celery and bay leaf. Drain and reserve liquid. Mash or force the beans through a sieve. Stir in the reserved cooking liquid and add the milk. Correct seasoning. Reheat the puree in the sunstove. Before serving add the butter, cut into small pieces, and blend well.

SOUP OF GREEN SPLIT PEAS

Wash the peas and soak them in water overnight. Drain. Place the peas in a black cooking pot.

To one cup of split peas add 2½ cups of water. When the soup has simmered, covered, for about one half hour add:

    1 small carrot, sliced
    1 onion, sliced
    2 tablespoon butter
    salt, pepper and a dash of sugar

Let this soup simmer for 2-3 hours or until the peas are soft. Remove from sunstove and force mixture through a sieve and return it to the cooking pot. Add ½ cup of consommé and ½ cup of light cream and one spoon of butter. Heat thoroughly.

If the soup has become too thick, thin it with milk or consommé. Before serving, work in the second tablespoon of butter.

Note: Yellow split peas and lentils can be prepared according to the same recipe.

CLEAR VEGETABLE BROTH

1 cup finely chopped celery
1 cup minced carrots
½ cup shredded spinach
4 cups water

1 teaspoon sea-salt
1 cup tomato juice
½ teaspoon sugar or honey

Cook vegetables for at least one hour then add tomato juice and sugar and simmer for 15-20 minutes more. Strain and discard the vegetables and use the Clear Broth as a basis for other soups or gravies.

The vegetables can vary according to availability. It is, however, important to mince and chop them finely in order to exact the utmost of nutrients and flavors, before discarding them.

ONION SOUP

Onion soup is a favorite 'stand by' and the recipes vary considerably according to country and tastes. The following onion soup was often served in our home. It is easy to prepare in the sunstove with the advantage that there is no onion smell in the house.

4 tablespoons butter
4 onions, finely sliced
2 tablespoons flour
6 cups beef consomme or
  broth

1 cup red wine
2 egg yolks
3 tablespoons heavy cream
2 tablespoons chopped
  parsley (optional)

Saute the onion in the butter until soft. Sprinkle with flour and stir well. Gradually add the stock and when the soup begins to simmer add the wine; continue cooking for a full hour. Correct seasoning with salt and pepper.

Before serving, beat together the egg yolks with the heavy cream and gradually add one cup of the hot soup to this mixture before adding it to the soup. Heat but do not boil.

TOMATO SOUP

1	tablespoon butter	5	cups water
1	large onion, chopped	1	bay leaf
6	tomatoes, quartered and peeled	1	small clove garlic
1	potato, peeled and cut in chunks	1	teaspoon salt, pepper to taste
		¼	cup raw rice

Cook the onion in the butter until soft. Add the tomatoes and continue cooking for about 15 minutes. Add the potato chunks, garlic, salt, bay leaf, and two cups warm water. Cover and simmer for about 40 minutes. Add remaining hot water and bring to simmer again. Discard garlic and bay leaf and strain the soup. Mash the vegetables and return with the liquid to the black pot. Add the rice and continue cooking until rice is done.

"A SOUP FOR DRUNKS"

In the good old days in Hungary a sauerkraut soup was considered as an antidote to a hangover. It was called Korhelyleves, which actually means a "soup for drunks." This sauerkraut soup was always served towards the end of a jolly party which usually lasted through the night. It was greatly appreciated by the young people, who had been dancing a wild Czardas for hours, accompanied by gypsy music—singing their heads off and slaking their thirst with fiery Hungarian wines.

To prepare an Hungarian sauerkraut soup don't rinse the kraut for the soup should be hot and spicy. When the sauerkraut has steamed for several hours, it is diluted with a broth made of pork knuckles or other smoked meat. Use one cup broth per serving. Thick slices of sausages (of the Polish Kielbasy type) are heated in the soup and sometimes sour cream is added also.

FISH AND POULTRY

SUN BAKED GROUND COD FISH

1 pound cod fillets (frozen)
3 oz. creamed cottage cheese (small curd)

1 egg
5 tablespoons bread crumbs
Seasoning to taste

Cube the frozen fillets and grind them finely

Mix the lightly beaten egg with the cottage cheese and spices and carefully fold the ground fish into the mixture.

Bake in a buttered form for one hour or until done.

Remarks: Fish prepared in this way has a good texture and flavor and is quite chewy. Further, it is filling without the need of adding potatoes, which is the general additive for fish cakes.

BASIC BAKED FISH

2 pounds fish, cleaned and trimmed
1 lemon
1 to 2 teaspoons salt

2 tablespoons butter or margarine (melted)
⅓ cup dry white wine

Line a shallow baking pan with foil and rub with butter or other fat. Rub inside of the fish with half the lemon and salt. Do not salt the surface skin.

Place a layer of unpeeled, thin slices of the lemon under the fish and brush well with the butter. Bake, covered, for about 15 minutes.

Pour wine over fish and continue baking until the fish is tender, about 1 hour.

If the fish is thick, cut little slits on each side to speed baking time.

Allow ½ pound of fish per person.

HUNGARIAN FISH DISH

6 fish fillets	1 teaspoon flour
2 teaspoons salt	4 slices of peeled tomatoes
1 tablespoon paprika	4 slices of onion
4 tablespoons melted butter	5 slices of cored, green
½ cup sour cream	peppers

Cut the fillets in half and rub them on both sides with a mixture of paprika and salt.

Arrange the fillets alternately with a slice of tomato, green pepper, and onion in a buttered baking dish. Sprinkle with the melted butter. Cover with a black lid and bake for 20 minutes. Pour the sour cream (mixed well with the flour) over the fish and vegetables and continue to bake, until fish flakes easily.

GEFILTE FISH

1 pound frozen haddock fillet	1 pint clam juice or fish broth
1 onion, medium	1 tablespoon gelatin
1 egg, beaten	salt, pepper, sugar
2 tablespoons cold water	
2 tablespoons cracker or matzo meal	

Cut the fish fillet in small pieces, place in food chopper or blender, add onion, and grind finely. Remove to a bowl, add the egg, matzo meal, salt and pepper to taste, and blend well. Form the mixture into small balls and place them in a black cooking pan and add the clam juice. Cover the pan and cook in the sunstove for about 1½ hours. Remove the balls and strain the juice. Add the softened gelatine to the juice, let cool slightly, and pour the juice over the fish balls. Chill thoroughly before serving.

CHICKEN KHORMA

A recipe from Kashmir

Khorma means meat marinated in buttermilk or yogurt.

1 large whole chicken breast	1 onion, chopped fine
½ cup buttermilk	1 pinch powdered ginger
2 tablespoon Ghee (clarified butter)	1 teaspoon salt
	1 teaspoon curry
2 cloves garlic, crushed	1 teaspoon turmeric

Cut chicken breast in 4 pieces and marinate them in the buttermilk mixed with one of the crushed cloves of garlic, at room temperature for 2 to 3 hours. Sauté the onion and remaining garlic in the Ghee until transparent. Add the spices to this mixture and stir well before adding the chicken pieces and the marinade. Cover with a black lid and cook for about two hours or until chicken is tender, stirring occasionally.

SUN CHICKEN

1 two to three pound chicken, cut into 8 pieces	1 tablespoon oil
2 apples, peeled, cored and sliced	1 tablespoon butter
	1 teaspoon paprika
juice and grated rind of 1 orange	1 teaspoon sugar

Rub the chicken pieces with the oil and dust with the paprika.

Arrange the apple slices mixed with the grated orange peel in the buttered black pan and cover them with the chicken pieces. Pour the orange juice over the chicken and dot with butter.

Close the pan tightly with the black lid and bake in the sunstove for about 1½ hours, or until chicken is tender.

COQ AU VIN

This famous chicken dish is easy to prepare in the sunstove.

Start with quartering a chicken weighing about 2½ lbs. (Discard the backbone, and use for gravy or soup base.) Rub into the chicken pieces one tablespoon each of oil and melted butter.

Coat the pieces lightly with flour mixed with pepper and salt.

Place the pieces in one layer in the pan, cover and roast for about one hour.

Meanwhile mix together:

1   small chopped onion
1   clove garlic, crushed
¼   teaspoon thyme
1   bay leaf

with ½ cup red wine, and let it stand while the chicken roasts.

Pour the wine mixture over the chicken and add 12 small peeled onions and 1 cup sliced mushrooms (optional).

Let this "Coq au Vin" simmer for 2 hours, or until the meat is tender.

SUNBAKED CHICKEN

Here is the recipe of the sunbaked chicken, which pleased Miss Mason's children so much. (See "The New Solar Generation," page 40.)

It is the most reliable method I know of cooking chicken, with sunshine. Even if some clouds appear while the chicken is in the oven—it always comes out perfect.

1 chicken, 1½-2 pounds	Salt and pepper
2 tablespoons flour	1 tablespoon oil
1 tablespoon paprika	1 tablespoon butter
½ teaspoon sugar	

Cut the chicken into 8 pieces. Rub each piece with oil, and toss or press the piece into the mixture of the flour, paprika, sugar, salt, and pepper. Place the chicken pieces side by side in a pan and dot with the butter. Cover and bake for 1½ hours or until done.

HUNGARIAN PAPRIKA CHICKEN

One January, when there was 2 feet of snow in the garden and an icy cold wind blowing (it was 26°F.), we succeeded, nevertheless, in cooking this delicious dish in the sunstove. The sky was sunny and the sunstove temperature was 280°F.

1 medium sized chicken	Salt and pepper
1 onion, sliced	1 cup sour cream
2 tablespoons paprika	butter
2 tablespoons flour	oil
1 teaspoon sugar	

Cut the chicken in eight pieces, rub them with oil and coat them with the mixture of flour, paprika, sugar, salt and pepper. Layer the onion in the pan, place chicken pieces on top and dot with butter. Cook for about 2 hours or until tender. Before serving stir in the sour cream and dust with paprika.

Menu for a Suncooked Festive Meal

This is the menu which was contemplated for the grand inauguration of the Sun Court at C.W. Princeton Division. (See "A Kind of Sun Saga," page 29.)

Soup Soleil
Sun-Roast Turkey
with
Trimmings
Sunbaked Peach Pie
Black Coffee

For weeks we were rehearsing for this gala performance to which the Press was to be invited.

SOUP SOLEIL

Made with a mixture of sun-dried carrots, parsnips, onions, celery and dried herbs.

Adjust quantities of each to your own liking. Soak the dried vegetables in a vegetable broth and simmer for a few hours. Puree the mixture and return it to the sunstove to be heated with a few pats of butter and additional seasoning to taste. Before serving, heavy cream and sherry can be added (about one tablespoon per serving).

SUN-ROAST TURKEY À LA CURTISS-WRIGHT

Rub the turkey inside and outside with a quartered lemon, pepper and salt. Place slivers of sundried orange peel and dried basil in the cavity. Baste with butter. Cooking time for a small turkey (under 10 lbs.) about 4 to 5 hours.

TRIMMINGS

4 cups cranberries
2 cups sugar

Mix the cranberries and sugar and let stand overnight. Place in sunstove. Cooking time, in clear weather, 2 hours. The berries have a clear red color and do not burst.

CREAMED ONIONS

Cook onions until tender but still firm. Drain and re-heat in a white sauce with some grated nutmeg.

SUN-BAKED PEACH PIE

Pie crust
Peach jam

Prepare the peach jam one day in advance. Use 2 lbs. peaches to 1 lb. sugar. Slice the peaches, mix with the sugar, and keep refrigerated overnight. Next day simmer until done. No stirring is needed.

Pre-bake the pie crust about 45 minutes and fill with the jam, cover with ribs of crust and bake until browned. (The ribs can be brushed with thin cream and sprinkled with sugar before placing the pie in the oven.)

Although this sumptuous meal was never served in the Sun Court as contemplated, the preparations and the testings resulted in valuable information about solar cooking, and we now have a multitude of scientifically controlled data on practically every food that can be cooked with sunshine.

MEAT

AUSTRALIAN BEEF STEW WITH PRUNES

1½ pounds beef, round roast
1½-2 tablespoons flour
1½ tablespoons brown sugar
1 teaspoon salt, pepper to taste
½ teaspoon curry
½ teaspoon ginger
¼ teaspoon dry mustard
½ teaspoon paprika
½ cup sherry or vermouth

½ cup tomato sauce
1 tablespoon Worcester-shire sauce
juice of 1 lemon
grated peel of 1 lemon
2 slices of bacon, cut into pieces
12 dried prunes, pitted and quartered

Cut the meat in thin slices, about 3-inches long and 1-inch wide. Mix the flour and the dry spices together with the dry mustard in a plastic bag. Add the meat slices and shake well.

Keep the bag in the refrigerator for several hours, or overnight.

Place the meat in a shallow black pan, mix the sherry, tomato sauce, lemon juice and Worcestershire sauce and pour over the meat.

When the sunstove reads 300°F, place the covered pan in the oven and simmer for 3-4 hours. If the stew appears too dry add some beef broth. At least one hour before serving add the prunes, bacon bits and the grated lemon peel. Stir and continue to stew, until meat and prunes are soft.

BURGUNDY BEEF

2 pounds of beef (preferably bottom round)
¼ cup flour
1 teaspoon salt
1 tablespoon paprika
½ teaspoon sugar
pepper to taste
2 medium onions, sliced
2 medium carrots, sliced

1 cup red wine
dash of thyme
a few sprigs of parsley
1 bay leaf
2 tablespoons oil
2 tablespoons butter
1 clove garlic, crushed
1 cup fresh, or ½ cup canned mushrooms (optional)

Cut the meat in 1½ inch cubes and coat well with one tablespoon oil. Mix together flour, paprika, sugar, salt and pepper and shake the meat cubes in this mixture. Toss the sliced onions and carrots and spread them in a layer over the bottom of a black pot, sprinkle them with the remaining oil. Place the flour-coated meat cubes atop of the vegetables, dot with butter, cover and roast until the meat gets color (about 1 hour). Now add the wine, mushrooms, bay leaf, thyme, and parsley. Stir it all together and cook for 2-3 hours, or until the meat is tender.

FLEMISH BEEF

2 pounds beef (chuck) cut in very thin slices
2 medium onions, sliced very thin
1 clove garlic, minced
1 tablespoon parsley, chopped

1½ tablespoon brown sugar
1 cup beer
½ teaspoon thyme
1 teaspoon marjoram
salt and pepper to taste

Sprinkle bottom of pan with the parsley. Arrange half the meat—a layer of onions and garlic—remaining meat—and sprinkle with thyme and marjoram. Mix the sugar with the beer and pour over the meat. Close the pan tightly with the black lid and bake about two hours or until meat is tender.

SUNBURGERS AND A SOLAR HAMBURGER COOKER

Few foods ever gave me so many headaches as when I first tried to "pan-fry" hamburgers in the sunstove. No matter what method I used they always turned out pale, tasteless and over cooked.

Finally, one day I found the key to the problem through making, out of a thin aluminum sheet, a special "solar burger cooker", as shown in Fig. 33. The cooker is equipped with a drip catcher so the burgers don't stew in their own juice. This did it! In 14 minutes the hamburgers were well done and had good brown color. Before placing the patties in the solar cooker each surface was coated with a little oil and a few drops of Kitchen Bouquet. Both parts of the cooker were pre-heated in the sunstove, i.e., the lid and the pan.

☆ ☆ ☆ ☆ ☆

In case a ready solar hamburger cooker is not available, it is easy to fabricate one by cutting a black baking sheet in two parts.

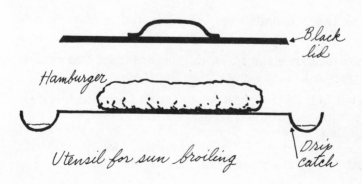

Black lid

Hamburger

Utensil for sun broiling

Drip catch

MEATBALLS IN TOMATO SOUP

1   pound chopped beef
1   small chopped onion
¾ cup bread crumbs
     garlic powder, salt and
        pepper

1   egg
     some Italian grated
        cheese
     chopped parsley
1   clove garlic, crushed
1   can tomato soup

Mix all ingredients, except soup, and form into balls. Place meatballs in shallow pan and add heated tomato soup. Cover and cook 1½ hours.

Contributed by Mrs. Terry Arnold.

SUNSTOVE BAKED MEAT AND POTATOES

A recipe from Alsace

½ pound pork
½ pound lamb
½ pound beef
1   pound potatoes (more
        or less)
2-3 onions

2   cloves garlic, crushed
1   cup dry white wine
spices: thyme, 1 bay leaf,
     and sprigs of parsely, tied
     in a muslin bag
salt and pepper to taste

Cube the meats. Make a marinade of the wine, the spices and one of the onions, finely chopped, and the crushed garlic.

Pour the marinade over the meat and refrigerate overnight.

Next day slice the remaining onions, peel and slice the potatoes. Remove meat from marinade.

Layer half of the potatoes in a well buttered black pot, top with the drained meat, onion, and end with the remaining potatoes. Remove the spice bag from the marinade and pour it over the dish. Dot liberally with butter. Cover well and bake for about 3 hours.

SOLAR BAKED HAM

It was an Easter Sunday when I baked a large ham—weighing 11 pounds and 3 oz.—in the sunstove. The sky was blue without a single cloud, but the air was quite chilly. Despite this the thermometer showed a temperature of 325° when I put the ham in the sunstove at 11 a.m.

The preparation consisted of wrapping the ham in aluminum foil after which I placed it in my largest black pan. A second pan was used as a lid, but it did not cover the ham completely. A meat thermometer was inserted.*

Once every hour we adjusted the stove so that it was focused perfectly towards the sun, and I also read the thermometer.

Around 3 o'clock the meat thermometer was at 160°F, which is the prescribed temperature for a baked ham. The ham had been in the oven for 4 hours.

As the ham was unwrapped only a little water had collected and no noticeable fat had seeped out.

We decided not to glaze the ham, but to eat it—"as is"—in order to be able to judge the flavor.

Everybody who tasted the sunbaked ham agreed that they never had eaten a better one. It was juicy and tender.

*It is advisable to use a meat thermometer for large cuts of meat such as ham or roast.

NAVAJO CHILI PORK

This recipe was tested during my Navajo trip in 1956. (See "The Development of the Sunstove," page 21.)

1½ pounds lean pork, cubed
1 tablespoon cooking oil
  flour for coating
1 tablespoon salt
1½ tablespoons red chili
  powder

1 teaspoon crushed oregano
1 clove garlic, crushed
1 tablespoon onion, chopped
3 tomatoes, peeled and diced

Roll the meat in the oil and coat lightly with salted flour. Add the onions and garlic and stir everything together in a black roasting pot. Cover with a black lid. When the meat begins to color, add the chili powder*, diced tomatoes, and oregano. Stir.

Cook for 1½ hours or until meat is tender, stirring occasionally. If sauce becomes too thick, add a little water.

*Reduce chili powder, if you don't care for hot food.

BRAISED CANTONESE PORK

1½ pounds pork shoulder
  sliced into thin strips
3 celery ribs, chopped
2 cloves garlic, crushed
1½ teaspoons dry ginger

1 tablespoon oil
2 tablespoons water
⅓ cup soy sauce
3 tablespoons sherry
2 tablespoons honey

Mix the water, oil, soy sauce, and sherry. Add the honey and mix well; add garlic and ginger. Add the pork and marinade for about 3 hours. Transfer pork and marinade to cooking pan; add the celery and bake, covered, for about 2 hours or until pork is thoroughly cooked.

If the sauce is too thin, thicken with 2 tablespoons cornstarch mixed in 3 tablespoons of water, and simmer until sauce is clear.

PAKISTANI LAMB

For visitors from Pakistan, I prepared the following lamb dish in the sunstove.

1½ pounds lean lamb, cut
    into 1 inch cubes
1   green pepper cored
    and chunked
1   small can pineapple
    chunks

Marinade:

¼ cup vinegar
⅓ cup oil
2   tablespoons fresh
    chopped mint
    liquid from small can of
    pineapple
    salt and pepper

Marinade the meat for several hours, or overnight, stirring occasionally.

Drain the meat and dust the chunks with cornstarch. Place in pan, cover, and heat until the meat begins to get color. Then add the chunks of pineapple and pepper and sprinkle the remaining marinade at intervals over the mixture, stirring carefully each time. Continue cooking until the meat is tender.

Serve in a ring of rice.

EGGPLANT WITH VEAL

From Greece comes this "solarized" dish.

2 pounds veal shoulder, cut in thin strips
2 tablespoons oil
1 tablespoon parsley, chopped
2 onions, minced
1 medium eggplant, pared and sliced

½ cup white wine
juice of ½ lemon
3 fresh tomatoes, peeled, seeded and cut in chunks
1 teaspoon tarragon
1 teaspoon basil
salt and pepper to taste

Cover the pared and sliced eggplant with salt and let stand for 30 minutes. Rinse well under running water. Drain and dry. Mix meat with half of the oil, and the onion with the other half. Place in pan in layers: veal, parsley, onions, and eggplant. Moisten with wine and lemon juice. Finish with tomatoes, and sprinkle with the herbs. Cover pan and bake in sunstove for several hours until meat is tender.

QUICHE LORRAINE

There are many variations on this classic dish. The following recipe I got from a Swiss lady who is a very good suncook. One can use either bacon or ham or a mixture of both.

Start with a pre-baked 9-inch pie shell.

Filling:
½ pound bacon or ham
¼ pound Swiss or Cheddar Cheese, shredded
2 cups milk
3 eggs

Fry the bacon and crumble it, or cut the ham into small pieces. Put the meat and cheese into the pie shell, scald the milk and let cool slightly, then add the eggs, beaten, and mix well. Pour the milk and egg mixture into the pie shell and sprinkle lightly with some more cheese. Bake in the sunstove until firm.

VEAL BIRDS

6 veal cutlets, sliced very thin and flattened with a mallet
½ lb. mushrooms
2 tablespoons grated onions
¼ cup chopped parsley

1 egg white
salt, pepper, flour
2 tablespoons butter, oil
½ cup white wine
¼ cup heavy cream

For filling: Chop all but six mushrooms finely with the chopped onion, parsley and seasoning.

Put aside the six mushroom caps.

Brush both sides of the cutlets with oil and seasoning. On the top side of the cutlets spread some of the filling. Roll each slice of meat and fasten with a toothpick. Brush the rolls with more oil, or melted butter, rub a few drops of soy sauce on each and flour them lightly.

Put rolls in a pan with the remaining butter and the mushroom caps, and bake under cover until the "Birds" get color, 2 to 2½ hours. Add the wine and continue cooking for about 30 minutes. Stir in the heavy cream and heat, but don't boil.

Serve the "Birds" with the gravy poured over them and a mushroom cap on each.

Note: Chicken breasts can be used instead of veal.

RICE AND PASTA

BASIC RICE

1 cup rice
2 cups water (more or less, depending upon
    the quality of rice)

Place in a low black pan and cover well with black lid. On a sunny day, rice will be ready in about 45 minutes.

RISOTTO

1	cup rice	salt and pepper
2½	cups consommé	3 tablespoons grated
1	clove garlic	Parmesan cheese
¼	cup butter	

Cook the rice in the consommé with the garlic clove. When the rice is tender, remove the garlic and fold in the butter and part of the grated cheese. Serve with grated cheese sprinkled over the dish.

RISOTTO MILANESE

1	cup rice	2 tablespoons tomato puree
¼	cup oil	2 tablespoons grated
½	cup chopped onion	Parmesan cheese
2	cups broth	salt and pepper to taste

Cook the onions in the oil until transparent, add rice and stir together with the onions. Pour warm broth on rice, stir again. Cover well. When almost ready, add tomato puree and spices (add more broth if needed). Sprinkle grated cheese over the Risotto.

RANI RICE

A dish with an Oriental flavor.

1 cup long grained rice	½ cup onion
2 cups chicken consommé	1 teaspoon curry
¼ cup butter or oil (or half oil, half butter)	1 teaspoon salt

Sauté onions in the butter until translucent, add the rice and stir. Let the mixture warm before adding the curry and the salt. Pour in the warm consommé, cover well with black lid, and bake until rice is tender (about one hour).

RICE AND PEAS

"Risi-Bisi", as this dish is called in Italy and also in many other countries, is very popular. It is easy to prepare and always comes out well in the sunstove and never sticks to the bottom of the pan. Since Risi-Bisi is so rich and substantial, it can be served as a main dish. It goes well with a tomato salad.

1 cup rice	2 tablespoons grated cheese (preferably Parmesan)
1 cup green peas (fresh or frozen)	½ teaspoon salt, pepper to taste
2 onions, chopped	
2 tablespoons oil	2 tablespoons butter
	1½ cups of warm water

Sauté the onions in the oil until they become translucent. Add the rice and peas, and mix thoroughly. Cover and cook for about 5 to 10 minutes. Add one and a half cups of warm water, place dish in sunstove and cook for about one hour. Add the butter, cheese, salt and pepper, mix well and serve.

MACARONI

To cook macaroni is considered easy. However, when I, for the first time, tried to cook macaroni in the sunstove several problems were encountered.

The following incident took place at the Solar Laboratory of New York University, soon after I had begun to work there as the associate of Dr. Maria Telkes. The Ford Foundation had just given a large grant to the University for the development of a sunstove for use in under-developed countries. As the reputation of this unusual cooking research was spreading, we received many visitors, mainly from foreign countries. Thus, one day, a lady who had something to do with Foreign Aid dropped in. She was a home economist with an assignment in Italy and had just returned to the USA for new instructions; among them was to study whether a sunstove would be of any use to Italy where at that time fuel was scarce and expensive.

The home economist cast a suspicious eye on the strange looking object with its shiny mirrors that did not resemble an ordinary kitchen stove at all. "Can one cook macaroni in that?" she asked; and in one breath she continued saying: "If not, then your sunstove cannot be used in Italy."

To my great chagrin, I had to admit that so far I had not found the time to make any experimental cooking with macaroni, or any other pasta, but I was convinced that it would be just as easy as cooking rice, which I had done repeatedly. (This last hasty remark I had, however, soon to regret.)

As soon as the home economist left the laboratory, I rushed to the nearest grocery store and bought a supply of macaroni.

A large pot filled with water was placed in the sunstove, and when the temperature had reached the boiling point (212°F), I added 2 cups of macaroni. At that point the water was just simmering, and in no way a "rolling boil" as conventional recipes call for.

After one hour, I checked on the result—no change—the macaroni was just as hard as it was an hour before. I gave it yet another hour, but to no avail. Nevertheless, I decided to give the macaroni still more time to get ready. After three hours, a change had taken place. The macaroni had begun to disintegrate—to melt! The whole dish had turned into soggy flour soup. With the best will in the world, I could not call it macaroni.

The first dismal failure, however, did not prevent me from trying again.

I therefore continued seeking new solutions but with very little success. After a whole week's struggle I was ready to give up, for it became evident that I could not bring the water to that vigorous boil, which is a prerequisite for all pasta cooking.

Then I got a bright idea: "Why not cook macaroni like one cooks rice?" In other words; to use only as much water as the product can absorb:

1 cup macaroni
3 cups hot water
1 tablespoon oil

The macaroni was tossed in the oil before the hot water was added. Instead of the high pot, which I had previously used, I cooked the macaroni in a shallow pan, with a black cover. The cooking time was one hour.

This method proved a complete success. The macaroni was cooked "al dente" and in addition it did not stick together at all.

Since that day I have never encountered any difficulty when cooking pasta in the sunstove. I have, however, found that different varieties require different amounts of water. For this reason, I always make a test cooking of a small amount before preparing a large dish.

Here is yet another example of this method of cooking macaroni:

2 cups elbow macaroni
3 cups hot water
2 tablespoons oil
½ teaspoon sea salt

The uncooked macaroni was first tossed with the oil in a shallow black pan, the hot water was added, and the pan was covered with the pre-heated black lid. Cooking time: 1 hour.

The macaroni was perfectly cooked. Not a drop of water remained in the pan. The macaroni was served mixed with two tablespoons of butter, grated cheese, and chopped fresh basil.

Another variation consists of adding both butter and grated cheese before the hot water is poured over the macaroni. The result is a finished dish, ready to serve. However, this method required stirring a few times during the cooking period.

One obvious advantage of cooking macaroni the "solar way," with controlled water quantity, is that all nutrients and flavors get sealed into the product and not thrown away with the usually discarded cooking water.

VEGETABLES

All vegetables that are cooked in the sunstove become delectable. They don't become mushy but remain firm, even after they are perfectly cooked.

Many vegetables like eggplant, squash, zucchini, etc. can be baked in their own skins before further preparations. This waterless method of cooking vegetables preserves the vitamins and enhances the aromas.

An especially tasty way of cooking vegetables is to slice them thinly, add butter, salt and a pinch of sugar, and let them stew in their own juices.

Another way is to cook carrots, or mushrooms in aluminum foil with a little butter and spices added. Place the individual parcels in a black pan and bake until done.

PICKLED RED BEETS

Wash 4 medium size beets. Do not peel or remove the roots, and leave about one inch of stem. Place the beets in a black cooking pot, cover and place in the sunstove for about 2 hours (do not add water). Remove the beets from the oven, let cool, and peel and slice them.

Pickling Mixture:

1 teaspoon dry English mustard	pepper to taste
1 teaspoon sugar	1 cup water
1 teaspoon salt	¼ cup vinegar

Dissolve the mustard powder and spices in a small amount of water before adding the vinegar and the rest of the water. Pour this pickling mixture over the beets and store them in the refrigerator. (If beets are to be kept for any length of time they should be placed in sterilized jars and processed in a boiling water bath.)

CELERY SALAD

One of the many advantages of cooking with sunshine is that so many dishes can be prepared in advance, particularly foods which improve when kept in the refrigerator for several hours or overnight. Such a dish is celery salad.

Place one or two small heads of celery in the cooking pot and add 2 cups of any good meat broth.

Cover and simmer for 1 to 1½ hours. Remove from stove and let celery cool in the liquid. Drain. (Save the liquid for soup or gravy base.)

Cut the celery into bite-size chunks. Marinate in a good French dressing and chill in refrigerator overnight or until thoroughly chilled. Serve on crisp lettuce.

PUREE OF GREEN CELERY TOPS

This pureed soup is an excellent way of using the green leaves of celery

10 celery ribs, tops and
   leaves chopped fine
 2 large potatoes, peeled
   cubed
 1 clove garlic, crushed

oil and butter
3 cups chicken (or beef) broth
   salt, pepper and your
      favorite herb mixture

Sauté the garlic and celery in butter and oil—add the potatoes, broth, salt, pepper, and herbs to taste and cook until the vegetables are sufficiently soft to press through a sieve (at least one hour). Return the puree to the black pot and add more broth for desired thickness. Correct seasoning. Serve piping hot. Can be topped with a spoonful of sour cream or yogurt.

PUREE OF BRUSSELS SPROUTS

1 pound Brussels sprouts
2 tablespoons butter
½ tablespoon flour
¼ cup water
¼ cup milk

1 egg yolk, beaten
2 tablespoons light cream
salt and pepper to taste
pinch of sugar

Cut the Brussels sprouts in half and simmer them in the water to which the butter is added. When the sprouts are soft, sprinkle with the flour and add the milk. Cover and simmer for about 20 minutes. Remove the pot from the sunstove and force the sprouts through a sieve. Beat the egg yolk and the cream separately and gradually add it to the pureed sprouts. Correct seasoning. Heat—but do not boil.

STUFFED GREEN PEPPERS

6 green peppers of
  uniform size
½ pound ground beef
1 egg
1 onion, chopped
¼ cup partly cooked rice
½ cup tomato sauce

¼ cup water
2 tablespoons oil
2 tablespoons chopped
  parsley
salt and pepper (garlic
  salt to taste)

Instead of blanching the peppers in water, as is customary for this dish, bake the whole peppers in the sunstove for about half an hour. Remove from oven, cool, and cut off the tops of the peppers. Scoop out the seeds carefully. Stuff the peppers with a mixture of half of the finely chopped onion, beef, rice, parsley, the beaten egg, salt and pepper. Place the peppers in a baking dish. Combine the tomato sauce, water, and remaining onion and pour this mixture over the peppers. Pour some oil on top of each pepper. Bake for about two hours or until meat is cooked.

RED CABBAGE

1	small head of red cabbage	1	apple
2	tablespoons salad oil	½	onion
1	teaspoon salt		juice of one lemon
1	tablespoon sugar	2	tablespoons cider vinegar

Remove outer leaves and shred the cabbage. Slice the apple and onion thinly. Coat the cabbage with oil and stir all ingredients together in the black cooking pot. Cover and cook for about 2 hours. Stir at intervals and add a little water if the dish appears too dry. Correct seasoning.

Red cabbage is especially good served with roast pork, duck, or other fatty meats. It also improves in flavor if made a day ahead of time.

VEGETARIAN SUN STEW

3	tablespoons oil	1	pear or apple, cubed
2	potatoes, cubed (medium size)	4	stalks swiss chard, cut in 1 inch pieces
2	onions, chopped	1	tomato, skinned and cubed
2	green peppers, sliced or chopped	¼	cup water
3	medium carrots, sliced		pepper, sea-salt, dash of cayenne, pinch of sugar

Toss vegetables in the oil, add water and seasoning, and simmer for 2 to 3 hours in the sunstove. Before serving, mix in 2 tablespoons sour cream and a teaspoon of soy-sauce.

VEGETABLE POT

"Lecso," an Hungarian dish

2 white onions
2 green peppers
4 tomatoes
2 to 3 tablespoons oil
   salt and pepper to taste.

Chop the onions and coat them well with the oil in the black cooking pot. Core and dice peppers and add to the onions. Cover and cook until the onions become transparent. Then add the peeled and quartered tomatoes. Mix together and simmer slowly until vegetables are soft. Season according to taste.

Variation: Add a quarter cup cooked rice to the vegetable mix and heat. Before serving mix in ½ cup of sour cream. Lecso is sometimes served with chunks of pork, sauteed separately with onion, garlic, and red pepper.

RATATOUILLE

¼ cup salad oil
1 large onion, sliced
2 cloves garlic, crushed
2 medium zucchini, cubed
1 small eggplant, peeled
   and cubed
2 green peppers, seeded and
   cut in strips
4 tomatoes, peeled and
   quartered
   flour, salt and pepper

Sauté the onion and garlic in a black pan until onion is transparent.

Flour the cubed eggplant and zucchini lightly and add, with the sliced peppers, to the onions. Cover and simmer in the sunstove for 1½-2 hours. Add the tomatoes and continue simmering until desired thickness.

Season with salt and pepper and sprinkle with chopped parsley before serving.

THE SOYBEAN

The soybean is a food almost as perfect as cow's milk. It is the only known food worthy to be labeled a true meat-substitute, for weight by weight it contains approximately twice as much protein as meat and four times that of eggs. Further, it contains an abundance of vitamins.

The draw-backs of this wonder food are that a) it requires a long cooking period, and b) it has a very insipid taste. The first obstacle can be overcome if the soybeans are cooked in the sunstove, where fuel and time don't matter. The problem with the flat taste can easily be remedied with careful seasoning.

Like all pulses, soybeans must be soaked overnight. (Some people recommend soaking them for 3 hours and freezing the beans for 12 hours before further preparations.) After soaking, during which time the soybeans swell to about 3 times their original volume, they must be drained and rinsed with fresh water.

To one cup of dry beans (about 3 cups soaked) add 1 to 2 cups of vegetable broth or meat stock and cook in the sunstove for 3 to 4 hours. (I always add ½ a lime and a bay leaf during this pre-cooking period, which are then removed.)

After pre-cooking, the soybeans can be prepared like Boston Baked Beans, or you can try the following recipe from China where for thousands of years soybeans have been used as a major source of protein.

CHINESE SOYBEANS

Proceed with the soaking and pre-cooking as described and when the soybeans are almost soft add:

- ¼ cup molasses
- 2 chopped onions
- 1 teaspoon powdered ginger
- 1 diced apple (cored)
- 2 tablespoons soy sauce
  salt and pepper

Continue to bake the beans in the sunstove for an additional hour.

OKRA TOMATO SUN BAKE

- 1 pound okra
- 4 tomatoes (or ¼ cup tomato paste and ¼ cup water)
- 3 medium onions, chopped
- 1 green pepper, chopped
- 1 clove garlic, minced
- 2 tablespoons oil
- 2 tablespoons butter

Wash the okra and remove stems. Skin and chop the tomatoes. Mix the onions, peppers and garlic together with the oil. Fold in the chopped tomatoes, and ¼ teaspoon sugar. Place the okra in the baking pan and sprinkle with salt and pepper and a pinch of cinnamon. Pour tomato-onion mixture over the okra and dot with the butter. Bake in the sunstove until the okra is tender.

CARROTS VICHY

- 1 pound small carrots, sliced thinly
- 3 tablespoons butter, cut into small pieces
- ½ cup water
- 1 teaspoon sugar
- ¼ teaspoon salt
- 1 teaspoon chopped parsley

Combine carrots, butter, water, sugar, salt. Simmer covered until tender and all water has been absorbed. Stir occasionally. Before serving add the parsley.

Variation: When finished add ¼ cup heavy cream, stir and cook for a few minutes longer.

SUN BAKED BERMUDA ONIONS

4 large bermuda onions
3 slices buttered toast
1 cup grated cheese
1 cup milk

3 eggs
3 tablespoons butter
salt and pepper to taste

Place the unpeeled bermuda onions in a pot, cover and pre-bake for about 30 minutes. Remove from sunstove, cool, peel, and slice the onions ½ inch thick. Cut the toast in triangles and place buttered side down in a pan. Arrange the onion slices over the toast and sprinkle the cheese on top.

In a separate bowl beat the eggs well together with the milk and spices. Pour this mixture over the onions. Dot with butter and sprinkle some paprika over the top. Cover and bake until the egg mixture is firm.

SOUBISE

Soubise *is a thick puree made of onions smothered in butter and thickened with rice and sweet cream. It is a savory accompaniment to many meats and can perk up even the dullest boiled beef or cooked mutton.*

1½ cups of finely chopped
   onions
3 to 4 tablespoons butter (or
   more)
½ cup cooked rice

3 to 4 tablespoons heavy,
   sweet cream
water or consommé
salt and pepper to taste

Simmer the onions in butter until they are very soft. Sprinkle with salt and pepper and add the cooked rice. Stir, and continue cooking. If the mixture appears too dry, then add more butter and a few tablespoons water or consommé. When the Soubise is quite soft, mash it with a wooden spoon or press it through a sieve.

Before serving, stir in some more butter and the heavy cream. Reheat but do not boil.

SUN BAKED CORN ON THE COB

When corn is boiled in water, much of the flavor, as well as nutrients, get dissolved in the water and wasted when it is discarded. However, when using the following sun baking process, no food value is lost:

> Husk and wash the ears, and before placing them in the black pot, rub them lightly with salt and brush generously with butter. Cover and bake, until done.

This 'waterless' method not only improves the flavor of the corn but also eliminates the application of butter at the table, which sometimes is kind of messy, particularly when small children are helping themselves.

CORN ON THE COB BAKED IN HUSKS

Here is another way of preparing corn on the cob:

> Remove some of the outer husks and open up the inner leaves until you reach the corn silk. Remove the silk and close the husks so that the corn regains its original shape. Rinse in cold water and place in a black pot. Cover and bake for about 1½ hours. Remove the corn from the oven and holding each ear with a towel shuck off the hot husks.

This method gives the corn a special fine flavor, and the texture of the kernels is different from those cooked in water.

BREADS AND CAKES

Before starting to bake breads, cakes, pies, etc., the sunstove must be pre-heated to·at least 300°F.

On a sunny day it wouldn't take any more time to bake a cake or a bread in the sunstove than in a gas or electrically heated oven. However, on a hazy day, or if unexpected clouds turn up, it will take longer and patience should be exercised.

It is better to use *two* smaller loaf pans, than one larger one.

All baking pans must be covered with a black lid. The bottom of the lid must be greased so when the cake or bread rises it won't stick to the lid. Remember, in a sunstove, you get the *most heat from the top* and not from the bottom. If no suitable black lid is available one can use any black baking sheet for covering the loaf or cake pan.

TIPS FOR GLAZING PIE CRUSTS

Very shiny: Use a combination of whole egg, egg yolk and a little oil.

Slightly dull: Use beaten egg alone or with a little light cream.

Crisp crust with no shine: Brush the crust with a little thin cream and sprinkle with sugar.

All pie shells should be pre-baked. It is better to use two smaller pie pans than one larger one.

Easy to Bake
BREAD
with only one rise.

This is a basic dough, which I have been using for baking
bread for many years, with sure results in the sunstove.

1 pkg. dry yeast	1 teaspoon salt
¼ cup lukewarm water	3-4 cups of regular flour
¾ cup buttermilk	1 to 2 tablespoons baking
¼ cup oil or melted butter	powder
4 tablespoons sugar	1 egg, beaten

Dissolve the yeast in the lukewarm water in a large bowl.
Warm the milk slightly together with the sugar and the
oil or butter. Add to the yeast mixture and add the
beaten egg. Beat in half of the flour, and mix until dough
becomes smooth. Stir in remaining flour, with the baking
powder, and knead about 200 turns on a generously
floured board. The dough should remain soft and slightly
sticky.

Roll dough into a rectangle, about 9 x 15 inches, and roll
this from long side as for a jelly roll. Fold ends under roll,
and place seam side down on well buttered baking pan.
Brush loaf lightly with melted butter. Cover, and let rise
in warm place until double in size, usually about one
hour.

To bake: Cover with a second black pan or suitable lid
and bake in the sunstove for one hour, or until loaf
sounds hollow when tapped.

The advantage of this *basic dough* is that it only needs
to rise *once*, and that it can be used, with some additions,
for many delectable baked goods.

Basic Dough Recipes:

DANISH COFFEE CAKE

Increase sugar in Basic Dough recipe to ½ cup and work in half a cup of raisins. When finished baking, sprinkle generously with granulated sugar.

CINNAMON ROLLS

Roll out Basic Dough thinly, and spread generously with soft butter. Sprinkle with crushed nuts, sugar and cinnamon. Roll up the dough as for a jelly roll and cut it in one inch thick slices. Place slices side by side in baking pan cover with black lid and bake for 1 hour.

FRUIT BRAID

Add to Basic Dough:

½ cup mixed candied fruit
¼ cup chopped pecan nuts
1 teaspoon grated lemon peel

Cut the dough in three strips and roll each separately. Twirl into a braid and place in a well buttered pan, cover and bake for 1 hour. Let cool and glaze with ½ cup confectioner sugar and 1 teaspoon milk. Decorate with candied fruits.

WHOLESOME WHOLE WHEAT BREAD

4½	cups whole wheat flour	1	tablespoon safflower oil
1	package dry yeast	1	tablespoon honey
1½	cups lukewarm water	1	teaspoon sea salt

In a large bowl dissolve the yeast in ¼ cup of water and one teaspoon of the flour. Let it sit for a few minutes until it begins to foam. Add the rest of the water, dissolve the honey in this mixture, and add the salt. Add 2 cups of the flour and beat with a wooden spoon until smooth. Cover and set in a warm place to rise for about one hour, or until the dough becomes foamy and light. Add more flour, a few spoonfuls at a time, and continue mixing until the dough is easy to handle. Place the dough on a floured bread board and knead it thoroughly, adding more flour, a little at a time, until the dough becomes elastic but not sticky. When the kneading is completed, the dough should be springy enough to almost resume its shape when pressed lightly with a finger. (The kneading requires 15 to 20 minutes and a lot of elbow grease.)

Shape the dough into two loaves and place into buttered or oiled baking pans (9 x 5 x 3 inches). Cover and set in warm place to rise until doubled in bulk. About one hour.

Place in pre-heated sunstove and cover with a pre-heated lid or black baking sheet. Bake until the crust becomes golden brown. Depending upon the sun, this may take about 1 hour or more. The bread is ready when it gives a hollow sound when tapped. Cool before slicing.

NAVAJO BREAD WITH WILD SAGE

1 package dry yeast
1 cup cottage cheese
1 egg
1 tablespoon lard, or other melted shortening
1 tablespoon sugar

2 tablespoon of dried, crushed wild sage
1 teaspoon salt
¼ teaspoon baking soda
¼ cup lukewarm water
2½ cups flour

Dissolve yeast in lukewarm water and beat eggs and cottage cheese until smooth.

Mix dry ingredients together and combine all ingredients in a large mixing bowl, adding the flour in small amounts, blending thoroughly after each addition until a stiff dough has formed. Cover the dough with a towel and allow to rise in a warm place until the dough doubles in size. Punch down and knead the dough for one minute.

Place the dough in a well greased pan, cover again and

let rise for about 40 minutes.

Bake, covered with a black lid, in the sunstove for about one hour or until the bread sounds hollow when tapped.

(This recipe was tested during my Navajo trip in 1956. See "The Development of the Sunstove", page 21.)

BANANA BREAD

1¾	cups flour	⅔	cup sugar
2	teaspoons baking powder	⅓	cup oil
¼	teaspoon baking soda	2	eggs lightly beaten
½	teaspoon salt	3	ripe bananas
½	teaspoon grated lemon rind or nutmeg	⅔	cups coarsely broken walnuts, or other nuts

Beat sugar and oil together thoroughly, add eggs and continue beating. Sift together the flour, baking powder, soda, salt, and grated lemon rind, and add this to the mixture, beating well. Mash the bananas to a pulp and beat them into the batter. Fold in the walnuts.

Grease one large or two medium size loaf pans and line bottom with heavy paper and grease well. Pour in batter and push it into the corners. Cover with a black lid that has been greased on the bottom side. Bake in pre-heated oven (300 °F) until cake tester inserted in center comes out clean.

Banana bread does not slice well when warm; therefore cool well and refrigerate before slicing.

Banana bread freezes well wrapped in aluminum foil.

APPLE BREAD

2 cups flour
2 eggs
2 teaspoons baking powder
1 teaspoon salt
½ teaspoon cinnamon
¼ teaspoon nutmeg

½ cup butter
1¼ cups peeled and finely grated apples
½ cup chopped pecans or walnuts
1 cup sugar

Cream the butter and the sugar until light and fluffy. Beat in the eggs, one at a time, beating thoroughly. Sift together the dry ingredients and fold them into the batter with the apples alternately, a few spoonfuls at a time. Fold in the nuts.

Pour the batter into two medium sized, very well greased, loaf pans and cover with a black lid, that has been greased on the bottom side to prevent sticking to the top of the loaf. Bake in pre-heated oven (300 °F) for 1½ hours or until done. Cool in the pan for 10 minutes before turning onto a wire rack. Let cool completely before slicing.

GLAZED LEMON BREAD

2½ cups flour
3 teaspoons baking powder
1 teaspoon salt
⅓ cup butter
1¼ cups sugar
2 eggs

1 cup milk
½ cup finely chopped walnuts
⅓ cup lemon juice
2 tablespoons grated peel

Cream the butter with one cup of sugar and one tablespoon of the grated lemon peel. Add eggs, one at a time, beating very well. Sift together the dry ingredients and add alternately with the milk and stir until batter is smooth. Fold in walnuts. Pour into two medium, well greased, loaf pans and smooth top of the batter. Cover with black lid which has been greased on the bottom side. Bake in pre-heated oven (300 °F) until cake tester inserted in the center comes out clean. Just before bread is ready, mix lemon juice and remaining ¼ cup of sugar and lemon peel and heat slowly until sugar melts. Glaze the bread with this lemon syrup immediately upon removal from oven and let cool in pan for 30 minutes. Cool on rack additional 3-4 hours before slicing.

APRICOT UPSIDE DOWN CAKE

1 pound dried apricots	½ cup light brown sugar
½ cup butter	½ teaspoon grated lemon peel

Batter:

5 tablespoons butter	2 tablespoons baking
⅔ cup sugar	powder
1 egg	¾ cup milk
2 cups flour	pinch of salt

Cover the apricots with water and soak for 2 to 3 hours. Simmer apricots about 30 minutes or until tender, depending upon the sun. Drain and cool.

Cream the butter and brown sugar together in an 8 inch square pan and stir in the lemon peel. Arrange the apricot halves over the sugar-butter mixture.

Batter: Cream the butter and sugar together and beat in the egg. Sift the flour together with the baking powder and salt, and add alternately with the milk to the creamed mixture.

Spoon the batter carefully over the apricots, cover and bake until done, at least one hour.

Turn upside down onto a warm plate. Can be served warm with whipped cream.

PUMPKIN CAKE

2	cups sugar	1½	teaspoon nutmeg
1	cup oil	1½	teaspoon cinnamon
4	eggs	1	teaspoon salt
2	cups pumpkin	1	cup chopped nuts
3½	cups flour	1	cup raisins (soak 15
2	teaspoons baking powder		minutes in hot water)

Mix sugar, oil and eggs; add pumpkin, raisins and nuts. Add dry ingredients and mix. Grease a cake pan, pour in the batter and bake about 1½ hours.

Contributed by Mrs. Terry Arnold.

FRUIT CAKE

½	cup butter	½	teaspoon ginger
2	cups sugar	2	tablespoons cinnamon
2	tablespoons honey	½	teaspoon ground cloves
6	eggs separated	1	teaspoon nutmeg
1½	cups flour	½	cup milk
1	tablespoon baking powder and a pinch of salt	2	cups chopped figs
		2	cups chopped raisins
		1	cup ground almonds

Cream together butter and sugar until fluffy, adding the six egg yolks one at a time.

Sift the flour with the baking powder, salt, and dry spices, and add alternately to the butter-sugar mixture with the milk. Stir in chopped figs, raisins, and ground almonds, lightly coated with flour.

Finally, fold in carefully the stiffly beaten egg whites. Bake in a very well buttered tube pan covered with a black lid for 2½ to 3 hours, or until tester comes out dry.

DESSERTS AND JAMS

STEWED APPLES WITH TANGERINE FLAVOR

Ordinary stewed apples often turn out to be a rather dull dish. However, with a small effort and some tangerine peels, stewed apples can be transformed into a delicious dessert.

Peel, core, and quarter the apples and place in the pan. Remove all the white pith from tangerine rinds. Cut the peel into small pieces and mix them with the apples. Add sugar to taste and pour a small amount of apple cider, or water mixed with lemon juice over the apples.

Let the apples stew, covered, in the sunstove until they begin to fall apart. Remove the pot from the oven. Pour the stew into a serving dish and cool. Serve ice cold, decorated with tangerine sections.

SUN BAKED APPLES EXTRAVAGANZA

Wash and dry 4 to 6 large apples, remove cores, seal bottom hole with a small pat of butter.

Pour into each cavity an equal amount of:

  Sugar
  Cinnamon
  Chopped nuts
  Raisins

Top the hole with a small pat of butter.

Set the apples in the baking dish and pour ½ cup of white or rosé wine around the apples.

Close and bake until apples are soft. Be prepared for a real extravaganza!

SUNBAKED APPLE BUTTER

Quarter the apples, or cut them in eighths. Remove the core but don't peel. Place them in a single layer in a black pan and bake them covered until they fall apart. Press the apples through a sieve. To each cup of apple puree add ½ cup of sugar.

Spices, like ground cinnamon or powdered cloves, can be added according to taste, or simply fresh lemon juice.

Heat the apple butter in the sunstove until all the sugar has melted. Serve when cooled, or store in sterilized jars for later use.

PLUM DUMPLINGS
"Zwetschgen Knoedeln"

Plum dumplings, or Zwetschgen Knoedeln, as they are called in Germany, can easily be cooked in the sunstove with the following waterless method.

2 cups Bisquick	10 small cubes of sugar
¾ cup milk	bread crumbs moistened
1 egg	with melted butter
10 small blue plums, pitted	

Mix the batter and drop one tablespoon full into each well buttered muffin tin. Place a cube of sugar in the center of each pitted plum. Press the plum into the batter, and cover the top with more batter. Make sure that each plum is carefully covered. Place the muffin tin in the sunstove at about 250 °F. Cook for 20 minutes or until a toothpick comes out clean when pushed into the batter. Remove the plum dumplings and roll into bread crumbs which have been moistened with melted butter, and sprinkle lightly with sugar. Serve warm.

BANANA FLUFF

4 bananas, mashed
4 egg whites, beaten hard with a grain of salt and a few
   drops of lemon juice

Fold the mashed bananas carefully into the whipped egg
whites. Turn into a well buttered dish, cover and sun-
bake for about 1 hour or until the center becomes firm.

CHEESECAKE

The original recipe for this delicious cheesecake requires
that the pie be placed in the oven and baked in a warm
water bath. When baked in the sunstove this step is not
necessary.

For pie crust mix ½ cup graham crackers with 2 tablespoons sugar and 2 tablespoons butter and pat into an 8
inch pie pan and bake for about 15 minutes. Set aside
and cool.

Filling:

grated peel of 1 lemon
grated peel of ½ orange
¾ pound cream cheese
½ teaspoon vanilla
¼ cup heavy cream

5 tablespoons sugar
2 large eggs
2 tablespoons sour cream
1 tablespoon milk

Add the cream cheese to the grated lemon and orange
rind and vanilla, beating well. Gradually add the heavy
cream and sugar, beating constantly. Add the eggs, one
at a time, beating well after each addition. Beat in the
sour cream and the milk. Continue beating but avoid in-
corporating air into the mixture.

Pour the cheese mixture into the prepared pie pan and
smooth the surface. Cover with a black lid and bake in
the sunstove until the center does not quiver when the
pan is shaken. Remove from oven and let stand for 10
minutes on rack. Invert and unmold while hot. Let stand
until cool.

FLOATING PEARS

6   firm pears
¾   cup port wine
½   cup water
½   cup sugar
3   tablespoons lemon juice
½   cup whipped cream

Filling:

1   tablespoon sour cream
1   tablespoon candied,
      chopped orange peel, or
      candied ginger
½   cup ground walnuts
½   teaspoon lemon juice

Peel and core the pears carefully, leaving the stems. Place the pears in a small pan in a single layer and cover with the wine and water mixture, sugar and lemon juice. Simmer under the black lid until a toothpick will push through a pear cleanly.

Remove and chill, preferably for 24 hours, spooning the wine over the pears at intervals.

Prepare filling and stuff the pears with the mixture. Place each pear on individual serving dishes, floating on a cloud of whipped cream.

Pour some of the wine over each pear or serve separately.

LIME PIE

Crumb pie shell:

1½ cups corn flake crumbs
½ cup sugar
½ teaspoon ground cinnamon
½ cup melted butter

Filling:

½ cup lime juice
1 can (14 oz.) sweet condensed milk
3 egg yolks, slightly beaten
3 egg whites
2 tablespoons sugar
1 tablespoon grated lime peel
1 cup heavy cream, whipped

To prepare shell: Combine the crumbs, sugar and spice in a bowl. Stir in the melted butter, mixing thoroughly. Line one large or two small pans. Chill about 20 minutes.

For the filling: Combine the lime juice with the condensed milk and egg yolks. Beat egg whites and add the 2 tablespoons sugar and continue beating until stiff peaks form. Fold into lime-milk mixture carefully and fill the chilled shell(s).

Bake in a 300 °F sunstove until firm. Cool well and cover with whipped cream before serving.

STRAWBERRY MERINGUE DESSERT

This is a light and delightful summer dessert served with fresh strawberries and whipped cream.

4 egg whites
1¼ cups sugar
½ teaspoon lemon juice
    one pinch of salt

Beat the egg whites with the salt until stiff, but not dry. Add the sugar, spoon by spoon, while constantly beating. The lemon juice is added drop by drop.

After all the sugar has been incorporated, continue beating for a while.

Butter and flour a wide, round cake form and fill it with the meringue. With a spoon make a dent in the middle by pushing the meringue mixture towards the sides, forming a ring.

Cover the form with a suitable black lid and bake for a long time at low temperature. The secret to making a good meringue lies in permitting it to dry, rather than bake, for a long time, in a slow oven. The sunstove is ideal for this purpose.

When the meringue feels dry, take it out, and while still warm, remove it from the form. Cool.

Just before serving, fill it with heaps of big juicy strawberries and whipped cream. Other fresh berries can be substituted.

PIÑON COOKIES

3 cups white flour
1 teaspoon baking powder
½ teaspoon salt
1 cup butter
¾ cup sugar
½ cup water (or more if needed)
½ cup shelled and chopped piñon nuts
cinnamon and sugar

Combine flour, baking powder and salt. In another bowl, cream butter and sugar until fluffy. Gradually sift in flour alternately with water until a stiff dough has formed. Add piñon nuts and blend thoroughly.

Roll out the dough on a lightly floured baking board to a ½ inch thickness. Cut with a cookie cutter, and sprinkle with a mixture of cinnamon and sugar. Place cookies on a well buttered cookie tin and cover with a pre-heated black lid or shallow baking pan.

The cookies are ready when they have a golden color.

DULCE DE LECHE

Concentrated sweet milk: A typical Argentine dessert.

2   cups milk
¾ cup sugar
1   teaspoon vanilla (optional)

Combine the milk, sugar and vanilla in a shallow pan. Cover and simmer for 2½ to 3 hours, mixing occasionally. Test the mixture once or twice to see whether the desired thickness has been reached. The Dulce de Leche is ready when a small amount of the mixture dropped into cold water forms a soft ball.

This concentrated sweet milk mixture is usually used for filling butter cookies.

To concentrate milk on an open fire is quite tricky. One must stir constantly to prevent scorching. I never had any trouble when preparing this dish in the sunstove.

PRUNE MARMALADE

½ pound prunes
½ pound sugar
4   oz. raisins
Juice of 1 orange, and its finely sliced peel
Juice of ½ lemon and its grated peel
2   oz. chopped walnuts.

Wash the prunes, remove the stones and cut the prunes into fine pieces. Add the raisins and the fruit juices together with the sliced orange peel and grated lemon peel.

Simmer in a covered black pot for about 1½-2 hours. Add the chopped walnuts and continue to simmer until the marmalade is thick enough to pour into sterilized jars.

MARMALADE OF CITRUS FRUITS

1 large grapefruit
1 large orange
1 lemon
peel of a second orange
water
sugar

Wash, dry and quarter the fruits and remove the pips.
Pass the fruit through a meat-grinder. Measure the pulp
and add twice the quantity of water. Tie the pips into a
muslin bag and add to pulp. Let stand over night.

Next day simmer this mixture in a black covered pot for
about two hours or until the peels are soft. Remove the
bag with the pips and measure again. Now add the same
quantity of sugar as the pulp and stir well. Continue to
simmer in the sunstove until a thin skin forms on the
surface of the marmalade, stirring from time to time. (If
sugar has melted, no stirring is required.)

Test: Pour one spoon of the marmalade on a cold plate
and let cool for 10-15 minutes. Pull a spoon through it
and if the line—or furrow—does not close, that is the
sign that the marmalade is ready.

SPICED RICE PUDDING

½ cup rice
2 cups water ⎫ (or 4 cups milk)
2 cups milk ⎭
½ cup sugar
½ teaspoon salt

1 tablespoon butter
3 egg yolks, beaten
½ inch long vanilla
   bean (optional)
nutmeg and cinnamon to taste

Mix the rice with the water and sugar and boil for about
half an hour. If only milk is used, add the rice to two cups
of milk and simmer for about half an hour. Add the remainder of the milk (warmed), butter and spices, and
cover well. Place dish in the sunstove and bake for
several hours—until a creamy and very soft pudding is

formed. (The timing depends upon the weather conditions—usually about three hours.) When I estimate the pudding is within a half hour of being done I add the vanilla bean. Let the pudding cool slightly, stir in the egg yolks, and serve. This pudding can be eaten warm with cold milk, or cold with whipped cream or with fruit compote. When well done it is creamy and golden yellow and is very nutritious.

My friend Terry Arnold is one of the most creative sun-cooks that I know. She is one of the few persons who has long cooked with one of my sunstoves.

Following are some of the dessert recipes that she has tested and given me permission to quote.

RICE PUDDING

1 cup sugar	4 eggs
2 quarts milk	cinnamon
1 cup rice	

Combine all ingredients and mix well. Pour into baking dish, cover with lid. Cook 1 hour.

RHUBARB PIE

2 cups diced rhubarb
1½ cup sugar
6 teaspoons tapioca

Add all three ingredients and 3 teaspoons butter together into a pie shell. Cover with strips of pie dough. Bake 1½ hours.

BOSTON CREAM PIE

½ package white cake mix
1 egg
1 tablespoon lemon juice

Mix ingredients, pour in a cake pan and bake one hour. Let cool. Slice through center.

Cream filling:

3 teaspoons corn starch
2 teaspoons butter
2 cups milk

2 egg yolks
vanilla to taste

Melt butter, add starch and milk, cook until thick, mix with egg yolks and vanilla. Cook 2 minutes, cool and spread between cake layers. Sprinkle confectioners sugar on top.

CHUTNEY OF MIXED FRUITS

This Chutney requires a long time to cook, and needs a lot of stirring when prepared on a conventional kitchen stove. It is therefore particularly suitable for sun-cooking.

½ pound apples
½ pound plums
½ pound pears or apricots
2 tablespoons raisins
1 pound sugar (can be half brown-half white)
½ cup vinegar
½ to 1 teaspoon chili powder

1 to 2 teaspoons curry powder
1 teaspoon caraway seeds, slightly crushed
4 cloves garlic, crushed
½ teaspoon powdered ginger
1½ teaspoons salt

Peel and core the apples and pears and cut them in small pieces. Stone the plums and cut in small pieces, mix the garlic with the salt and the spices and stir into the fruits together with the sugar and vinegar. Let stand until sugar melts. Place in a black pan, cover and simmer in the sunstove. When fruits are softened, crush them slightly with a wooden spoon. Cool before bottling.

BOILING WATER

One might assume that nothing could be easier than to boil water. It certainly is provided one uses an ordinary heat source, like gas or electricity. But with a sunstove, water boiling was not so easy, at first. Water is a bad heat conductor and if one uses a regular vessel, it takes a long time to bring water to a boil.

Thus, this simple task of boiling water turned out to be quite a tough task. It was only after several trials and errors that I found a solution to the problem.

The experimental solution consisted of stuffing some well cleaned, noncorrosive metal scraps, into a shallow, closed, black pot, which was then filled with water. The metal parts transferred the heat from the lid into the water, which thus was brought to a boil much faster than hitherto had been possible. This method lacks simplicity and aesthetic appeal, however, because the metal scraps must be strained out. A better way of boiling water in a sunstove is to use a utensil specially constructed for this purpose.

This *solar tea kettle* is made of metal, and the top of the vessel is equipped with inner fins, which conduct the heat into the water. Like a regular tea kettle, it has a funnel or spout, for filling or pouring the water—it has also a regular whistle, which can be heard blowing through the glass window. It is a perfectly safe and convenient way to boil water with sunshine.

COFFEE BREWING IN THE SUNSTOVE

Any metal coffee percolator can be used for making coffee in the sunstove, provided that the pot has been blackened with black paint. A glass percolator, which takes advantage of the heat-absorbing color of the coffee, is also good. It is easy to observe through the glass when the coffee begins to perk. It is not a very rapid process—but it works.

There are, however, other ways of cooking coffee, like the method I learned in Brazil, which goes as follows:

A KIND OF BRAZILIAN COFFEE

While I was in Brazil, that land of coffee and colors, I stayed with some friends who lived in one of the suburbs of Sao Paulo. Here I learned to brew coffee in a Brazilian way, which I since have adapted for solar cooking.

This Brazilian way of brewing coffee was that in the evening the lady of the house poured and carefully measured ground coffee into a small stocking of child size, and then tied it closed with a string, letting the ends of the string hang over the edge of the coffee pot. Premeasured cold water was next poured over the stocking, whereafter the brew was allowed to steep during the night.

The next morning the coffee pot, complete with stocking, was heated, but only just to the boiling point, when the stocking was fished out with the string.

This coffee was served for breakfast. It was very strong but not bitter, and had a delightful aroma. We drank it half and half with hot milk after which the stocking was emptied, washed, dried and reused.

I have since repeated this stocking-coffee-cooking method in the sunstove with excellent results using a pyrex pot for this purpose, which permits one to observe when the coffee is ready without having to open the oven door and look. As the water becomes black from the coffee, it absorbs the heat of the sun relatively quickly.

MILK

Here in America we are very lucky to have always at hand clean and pasteurized milk which can be safely drunk. In many parts of the world this is not the case.

For those without access to pasteurized milk, to pasteurize milk with solar energy proves to be simple. It does not take more than half an hour to pasteurize one quart of milk in this area 25 miles south of New York City.

Pasteurization of Milk in the Sunstove

For the experiment 1000cc (l liter) milk was used. The test were done in late July.

TIME	TEMP.°F in milk	TEMP.°F in oven	Ambient TEMP.°F
2:30	45	300	82
2:35	70	290	
2:40	98	290	*Weather:*
2:45	105	290	Fair, with
2:50	125	290	light clouds
2:55	138	290	
3:00	148	290	

Total Time: 30 minutes

For this experiment a regular tea kettle was used. It had a diameter of 8 inches and was painted black. The whistle was removed and replaced with a rubber cork, through which a long stemmed thermometer was inserted which could be read through the window.

APPENDICES

Heat Storage

"What can one do when the sun disappears?" is a standard question, to which the answer is, "One can use *heat storage.*"

A heat storage can be a material, like bricks, stone, sand, oil, or certain chemicals, which absorb the heat of the sun as long as it is shining, and release it during hours of no sunshine.

Heat storage is desirable, for it can extend the cooking time for about one hour after sunset, and keep the food warm for an additional hour.

But heat storage made of any of the above-mentioned materials will, obviously, add to the expense of the sunstove as well as to its weight.

The most efficient is a slab filled with chemical heat-storage, but this is by no means an easy item to fabricate.

For this country a suitable electric heating pad, which could be plugged in after sunset, would serve a good purpose. But where no electricity is available, the best method (as previously mentioned) is to remove the mirrors and cover the sunstove with a blanket, or pillow and to use it as a "hot box".

Heat Storage Test in the Sunstove

Two pounds of a chemical heat storage, mainly Na_2So_4 (sodium sulfate, or Glauber's salt), having a transition temperature of 350 °F, was encased in a flat metal container.*

TIME	OVEN TEMP. °F	WEATHER
11:30		clear
12:30	250	hazy
12:45	275	hazy
1:35	300	hazy
2:10	325	hazy
2:35	350	clearing
	Mirrors removed, stove covered, by blankets.	
3:00	350	clear
3:35	350	clear
4:00	280	clear
4:35	250	clear

For over two hours the oven temperature was over boiling temperature (212 °F). 150 °F is considered to be "hot food".

*Patent of M. Telkes.

Recorded Results of Solar Cooking

Conducted at Curtiss-Wright Corporation Solar Laboratory, Princeton, New Jersey, in the autumn of 1958.

Please note how well the different foods cooked in spite of the low temperatures.

It is a good habit to keep track of one's suncooking.

| Type of Food | Quantity | TIME | | | TEMP. | | |
		In	Out	Total	In	Out	Weather

Location: Outside Temperature:

Details of Food Preparation:

Remarks on Results:

Location: Princeton, New Jersey

| Type of Food | Quantity | TIME | | Weather |
		In	Out	
Beef stew (cubed top sirloin)	1 pound	2:30	5:15	Sunny
	Temp:	275	275	

Details of Food Preparation: The beef cubes were shaken in a mixture of flour, paprika, and salt. After one hour, sliced onions and carrots were added.

Remark on Results: The meat was tender and juicy, not enough seasoning.

Location: Princeton, New Jersey

| Type of Food | Quantity | TIME | | Weather |
		In	Out	
Whole chicken	3 pounds	11:35	1:45	Clear-sunshine
	Temp:	350	300	

Details of Food Preparation: The chicken was rubbed with butter, mixed with paprika. No basting during roasting.

Remarks on Results: Perfectly cooked, good color.

Location: Princeton, New Jersey

| Type of Food | Quantity | TIME | | Weather |
		In	Out	
Chicken breasts (small)	4	1:15	2:45	Clear-sunshine
	Temp:	325	310	

Details of Food Preparation: The chicken breasts were rubbed with butter and a mixture of: 2 tablespoons flour, 1 teaspoon paprika, ½ teaspoon salt, dash of pepper.

Remarks on Results: Very good and juicy.

Location: Princeton, New Jersey

| Type of Food | Quantity | TIME | | Weather |
		In	Out	
Lentil soup	1 cup dry lentils	10:05	11:30	Clear sunshine
	Temp:	300	300	

Details of Food Preparation: The dry lentils were mixed with: 5 cups water, onion flakes, pepper and salt.
Remarks on Results: The lentils were soft. Good taste.

Location: Princeton, New Jersey

| Type of Food | Quantity | TIME | | Weather |
		In	Out	
Shrimp	1 pound	10:30	2:20	Hazy and
	Temp:	225	200	Windy

Details of Food Preparation: The unpeeled shrimps were coated with oil, sprinkled with caraway seeds and garlic salt.
Remarks on Results: Good, with firm texture.

Location: Princeton, New Jersey

| Type of Food | Quantity | TIME | | Weather |
		In	Out	
Scallops	1 pound	12:35	2:15	Light clouds
	Temp:	300	250	

Details of Food Preparation: The scallops were rolled in flour, mixed with paprika and salt, and dipped in beaten egg. A small amount of pre-heated oil was added to the scallops.
Remarks on Results: Good and not chewy. A pan with a drip catch would be better because of the liquid.

Parabolic Solar Cookers

Parabolic solar cookers are gaining in popularity, particularly among hikers and campers who understandably appreciate an item with which they can quickly warm a can of soup, cook some franks and brew a cup of coffee. The efficiency of a parabolic solar cooker is so great that it can bring a quart of water to boiling in 15 minutes.

The late solar scientist, Professor Farrington Daniels, stated that: "A fairly crude parabolic collector made of aluminized plastic film, lining a plastic shell, can produce temperatures of 500 °C (932 °F) or more."

Another pioneer in the solar field, Dr. George O.G. Lof, has introduced an interesting, umbrella-type, parabolic solar cooker, principally designed for recreational use. The entire cooker, including reflectors and stand, weighs about 4 pounds and can be folded into a carrying case. The reflecting material is made of aluminized Mylar polyester film laminated to a rayon fabric. The opened reflector presents an effective are of 11 square feet. A 9-inch square grill may be secured to the shaft.

It was found in field testing that clay pots can be used just as well as vessels of aluminum or steel. It is, however, important to blacken the bottom of the pots and pans.

Although parabolic solar cookers have many advantages, since they can produce high temperatures almost immediately—they have also some drawbacks: they can only be used when there is a perfectly clear, blue sky and no wind, because in a strong wind the reflectors vibrate so much that the food can spill. Further, the stove must be moved constantly to track the sun, whereas stoves with flat plate collectors only need to be focused about once in an hour, and are less affected by weather and wind. There is also the risk that people can get blinded if the reflectors are incorrectly focused.

The first circular parabolic solar cooker was developed

at the National Physical Laboratory of India at New Delhi. But though it was an inexpensive and a needed item, it was not favorably received, because it could not be adapted to native cooking habits. Another reason for its rejection—I was told—was that monkeys learned to steal the food from the kettles.

But one thing is sure, the parabolic solar cooker is here to stay, and hopefully will be further improved. It is a welcome solar item to those out-door enthusiasts who want to prepare for themselves a quick lunch in the sun.

REFERENCES

Solar Cooking Ovens, Maria Telkes, in *Solar Energy,* January, 1959.

Practical Solar Cooking Ovens, Maria Telkes and Stella Andrassy, presented at the United Nations Conference on New Sources of Energy, 1961.

Laboratory Notebooks, Stella Andrassy, Solar Electric Laboratories, Kingston, N.J. 1954-1978. (Unpublished)

The Solar Food Dryer Book, Stella Andrassy, Morgan & Morgan, 1978.

RECIPES INDEX